EXPERIMENTS

IN SKY WATCHING

Experiments
in Sky Watching

by Franklyn M. Branley

Illustrated by Helmut K. Wimmer

THOMAS Y. CROWELL COMPANY

New York

for Margaret

Acknowledgments

It is a pleasure to give full credit to the following individuals and companies for their kind cooperation:

C. W. Gartlein of the IGY Auroral Data Center, Cornell University, Ithaca, New York, who furnished information concerning the observing of auroras and the recording of data.

Fred L. Whipple and his publishers, Harvard University Press, for permission to adapt the table of planet positions which first appeared in their volume *Earth, Moon and Planets*, copyright 1941 by The President and Fellows of Harvard College.

Henry M. Neely and his publishers, Harper & Brothers, for their permission to adapt the table converting star time to civil time which first appeared in their volume *Primer for Star-Gazers*.

Stanley P. Wyatt, Jr., Associate Professor of Astronomy at the University of Illinois, for reading the manuscript and offering valuable suggestions.

CONTENTS

EXPERIMENTS

IN SKY WATCHING

FIRST STEPS

1

TYCHO BRAHE, a Dane who lived in the sixteenth century, was one of the world's greatest astronomers, yet he did his work before the telescope was invented. He succeeded without a telescope because he was a careful observer of the sky, and because he was a painstaking recorder of his observations. As a result of the great precision and accuracy that Tycho achieved with crude instruments, his tables of the positions of the stars and planets are highly respected by astronomers of today who work with extremely fine tools.

The experience of this Danish astronomer, and of thousands of other observers, proves that one can study the sky and learn much about it by using his eyes alone. Indeed, the eye is man's most important astronomical tool. A trained eye, together with a good measure of curiosity, is all you need to make many discoveries of your own about the sky and the objects in it.

Most of us look down or straight ahead much of the time. We look into the sky only when we hear an airplane or when an artificial satellite is expected to be visible. Other people look into the sky and study it; they look for changes in the positions of the sun and moon; and they recognize planets, stars, and constellations.

People study the sky because they are curious about their surroundings. Perhaps you, yourself, have wondered why the stars appear to change position, or you may have wondered why the appearance of the moon changes from night to night, and from week to week. If you have wondered about such things, then you have curiosity, a requirement for successful sky watching.

Through your study of the sky you will get a better understanding of this planet on which you live. You will improve your understanding of our solar system, of the place of the solar system in the Milky Way galaxy, and of the place of our galaxy in the universe. The experiments in this book will help you to find out information for yourself. They will help you to learn many interesting facts about the world that is round about us.

FINDING DIRECTION AND LOCATION

The first step in sky watching is to locate yourself properly, both in space and on the earth. In order to do this, you have to determine north, south, east, and west. One way of doing so is by watching your shadow. If you live in the United States, your shadow is fairly long in the morning and the afternoon. It is shortest at noontime, when your shadow points directly toward the north. This is because the sun is directly toward the south.

Face toward north while holding your arms outstretched sideways. Your right arm points toward the east and your left arm toward the west. Your back is toward the south.

You can find directions more accurately by the shadow method. Fasten a stick upright at the center of a board about eight inches square. You can do this by putting a screw up through the center of the board. Be sure the stick is vertical to the board by checking it with the edge of a book. Take the shadow stick outside and place it on the ground. The board should be level. The stick will cast a shadow whenever the sun is shining. At noontime the shadow will be the shortest; this shortest shadow is a north-south line.

You can determine direction also by using your knowledge of

the place of sunrise and sunset. If it happens to be evening when you are finding direction, look around the sky for the brightest area. You know that the sun sets toward the west. Therefore, the brightest area will be where the sun has just set; it will be the west. The sky darkens first along the opposite horizon, toward the east.

At night, you can determine directions by using the stars. The aid used most often is the Big Dipper. Throughout Canada and most of the United States, the Big Dipper is above the northern horizon all during the year. The two stars at the end of the Dipper are helpful in finding Polaris, which is our North Star. In your imagination join together Merak and Dubhe, the stars at the end of the bowl. Continue this line until you reach the first bright star. This is Polaris, the North Star. The apparent distance between the Dipper and Polaris is about five times the distance between Merak and Dubhe. If you are facing Polaris, south is at your back, east is on your right side, and west is on your left.

As you become more skillful in observing, you will want to locate objects in the sky more precisely. One way of doing this is by telling in degrees how far around the horizon from north the object is, and by giving its location between the horizon and the imaginary point in the sky that is directly overhead—the zenith.

Everything in the sky can be located by giving its position with respect to this circle of the horizon. A circle is divided into 360°. The horizon is a circle, so it may be divided into 360°. North is 0°; east is 90°; south is 180°; and west is 180° plus 90°, or 270°. As we look from west toward the north, we approach 360°, so you might think of north as being both 0° and 360°. The position of an object relative to north is its *azimuth*.

In order to locate an object, you must know not only its azimuth but also its *altitude*, where it lies between the horizon and the zenith. If the object is on the horizon, the altitude is 0°; if it is overhead, the altitude is 90°. Halfway between the horizon and overhead is 45°; one third of the way is 30°, and so on.

The illustration shows the azimuth and altitude of an object in the sky — in this case, 0° azimuth and 45° altitude.

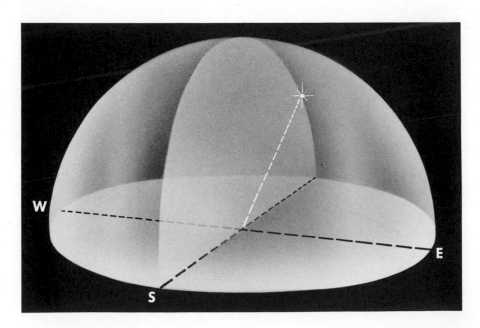

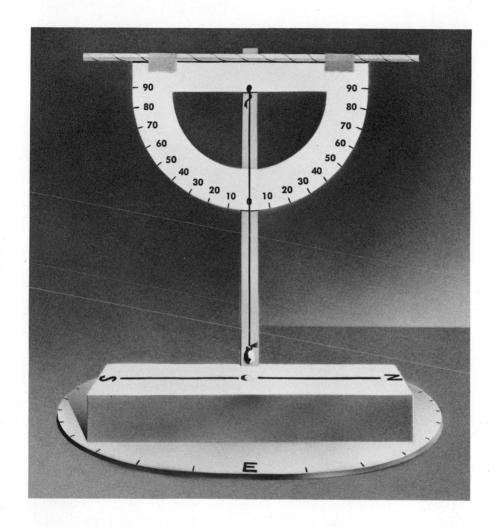

You can make a device for determining azimuth and altitude by following these directions: Use a piece of wood about 6 inches square and at least an inch thick for a base. The wooden upright of your instrument should be a foot long, an inch wide, and ¼ inch thick. Notch the base and set the upright in the notch, fastening it with two screws.

If you do not own a large protractor, you can cut one from cardboard as shown in the illustration. If you make one, it should be of heavy cardboard, 4 inches from one side to the other and half a circle. Divide the curve as indicated, and number from 0 to 90 in both directions. If you are using a metal protractor, cover the numbers that appear on it and renumber as indicated in the illustration. Drill a hole through the straight part of the protractor, placing the hole on the line joining the zero readings. With cellulose tape, fasten a large soda straw along the edge of the protractor. Nail the protractor to the upright with a fine nail. The protractor must be free to move. The nail should project somewhat because you have to fasten a thread to it. Tie a thread to the nail and fasten a small weight to the end of the thread. You might use a small lead sinker as a weight.

Your instrument is now ready to use for finding the altitude of an object. Take the instrument outside and set it on a level place, such as the top of a fence post. Sight through the soda straw at a star. The number that is directly beneath the thread is the altitude of the star. Use a small flashlight to read the dial. To use this instrument correctly, you *must* level the base. An ordinary carpenter's level will help you to determine this.

By modifying this instrument slightly, you can use it to find the azimuth of any object in the sky. Follow the same procedure as for a star.

Draw a line on top of the base from one end to the other, and running through the center. Letter an *N* at one end and an *S* at the other. Cut a 12-inch circle from heavy cardboard. Divide the circle into quarters and then into eighths. Each of the eighths should then be divided into three equal sections; each one being 15°. Number them in order, beginning with 0, 15, 30, 45, 60, 75, 90, 105, and so forth. Divide the spaces between into thirds, each division representing 5°.

Draw two diagonals on the base of the instrument. Drill a hole through the point where the lines intersect — the center of the block. Fasten the circle to the bottom of the block with a brass paper fastener.

Find the azimuth of an object as follows. Sight Polaris through the soda straw. *N* on the base is now toward the north. Line up 0 on the cardboard disk with the *N-S* line on the block. Without moving the cardboard disk, swing the instrument around until you can sight the star that you want to study as directed for Polaris. The line on the block will match some line on the disk. The line on the disk is the azimuth of the star. If you cannot see the figures, use a flashlight. Cover the lens with red cellophane.

THE SUN

2

Now THAT you can find directions, you can make some interesting discoveries about the sun. Of course, the discoveries that you make will not reveal knowledge entirely new to man and to astronomy. Nevertheless, from your standpoint, they are truly discoveries; and when you make a discovery you experience the thrill of finding something new, just as men did long ago. For example, you can discover that the sun really does not rise in the east and set in the west, as people often say it does. The sun rises in the east and sets in the west only on the first day of spring and the first day of fall. You can prove this for yourself by making observations as directed below.

Determine east and west on your horizon. Perhaps a tree, house, or hill is close to directly east or west. Use this as a marker to help you keep the directions in mind. Make a map of the eastern sky line showing trees, buildings, or other features, and another one of the western sky line. Each day notice where the sun rises and sets, and then put the date in the proper position on each map. Do this for a day or two, skip a week, and then make new observations while standing in the same location where you made the other ones. (For example, if the first observations were made from your front steps, then make all other sightings of the rising and setting sun from the same front step.) Again mark the locations of the rising and setting

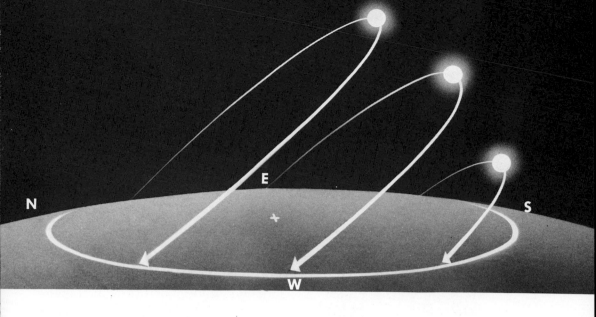

sun on your maps. If you wish, skip a week or so and then make some more observations.

You will find that during winter the sun rises south of east, and it sets south of west. It is farthest south on the first day of winter — around December 21. As we move toward spring, the sun rises nearer to directly east. It rises due east on the first day of spring. Then, as we approach summertime the sun rises north of east. It reaches the northernmost location on the first day of summer — around June 21.

Here is another way of proving that the sun sets at different locations throughout the year. Look through a window that faces toward the west and notice where the sun sets. Line up that spot with a tree, hill, or building. Paste a piece of paper on the window, mark the exact spot, and print on it the date of the sunset. A week later, watch the sunset again from the exact same location. Paste another piece of paper on the window and label it. There will be a difference between the two positions. Continue doing this and it will be quite apparent that the position of the setting sun changes throughout the year.

The sun always rises *toward* the east and it always sets *toward* the west. So it is not correct to say that the sun rises *in* the east and sets *in* the west, except on the first day of spring (about March 21) and the first day of fall (about September 23).

The position of the rising sun changes throughout the year because during summer in the northern hemisphere the axis of the earth is tilted toward the sun — the sun appears higher in the sky. In winter, the axis is tilted away from the sun, and so the sun appears lower in the sky.

There is an imaginary line in the sky directly overhead that passes from the North Pole to the South Pole. This line is called your meridian. When the sun is on the meridian, it is noontime as reckoned with a sundial. Also, it is noontime when the sun is halfway between the eastern and western horizons. Or, you might say that it is noontime when the sun reaches the highest position above the horizon for that day.

The noontime position of the sun on the meridian — its noontime altitude above the southern horizon — changes throughout the year. It is interesting to make a chart that shows the position of the noonday sun at different times. Look toward the south and draw a picture of the horizon, showing trees, buildings, and hills.

When your watch reads 12 o'clock (1 o'clock if you are on daylight saving time), note the location of the sun. Draw the sun on your map, and put the date alongside the picture. About a week later, stand in the same position at noontime, notice the position of the sun and then draw another picture on your map. Continue doing this for four weeks.

The noonday sun will be at the lowest elevation from the southern horizon on the first day of winter. It will be at the greatest height above the southern horizon on the first day of summer.

(CAUTION: Never look directly at the sun unless your eyes are protected. Sun glasses do not provide enough protection. You must look through a piece of smoked glass. Get a piece of glass about 3 inches square. Hold the glass in a candle flame, moving it continuously. The glass will become coated with soot. When you look at the sun through this heavily smoked glass you will not endanger your eyes.)

You might be aware of these variations of the angle of the sun above the southern horizon by casually observing the sun; however, if you keep records of solar positions, the changes will be most apparent. When you make readings of the angle of the sun above the horizon, record the information in a notebook. You should include the date of the observation, the angle above the horizon, the place where the observation was made, and the latitude of the place.

You can measure the angles with the instrument referred to earlier, or you can make one with two 12-inch rulers, or pieces of wood about the same size and length as rulers.

Cut the corners from the ends of the rulers and round them off with sandpaper. Fasten one ruler to the other with a small brad or nail. Put the nail through the rulers at the end at the half-inch mark and through the central point between the top and bottom edges of the rulers. But do not drive the nail all the way through them. It should extend about one-quarter inch above the top ruler. Hammer a brad into each ruler at the eleven-inch mark, halfway between the edges. The heads of these brads should extend out about one-quarter inch also.

Fasten a 6-inch square of cardboard to the back of the bottom ruler, and then you are ready to determine the angle of the sun above the horizon.

Hold the rulers close to your eye and sight along the bottom ruler, lining up both brads with the horizon, allowing for any elevation above the ground that you are standing on. This gives you a base line that is parallel to the surface of the earth. Have someone hold the smoked glass in front of your eye and then, without moving the bottom ruler, move the top one until the two brads line up with the sun. Holding the rulers in the same relative positions, lay them on a flat surface and draw lines on the cardboard: along the top of the lower ruler, and along the bottom of the ruler that pointed toward the sun. Remove the cardboard from the ruler and measure the angle with a protractor.

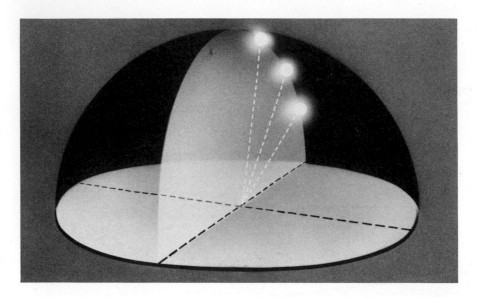

Those people who live at 40° north latitude will find that the summer sun is about 73° above the horizon, the spring and fall sun about 50°, and the winter sun only about 27°.

As mentioned earlier, never look at the sun except through a piece of smoked glass. If you have been using the glass described earlier, you have probably found that it needs more smoking, because soot rubs off onto your fingers or your nose. To avoid this, place a second glass plate over the smoked one and bind the two together with cellulose tape. Now you can handle the viewing glass without any of the soot rubbing off.

We cannot make any promises; but, if you look at the sun through your glass, you may be able to see a sunspot, if conditions for viewing are ideal and if there are particularly large spots on the sun. Usually the sun's surface appears to be uniform. When you see a sunspot, you will observe a small, black region. Sunspots occur quite often; however, there are periods of especially strong activity that occur about every eleven years. The last period of high activity was in 1957-1958.

Sunspots are clues to disturbances on the surface of the sun. These disturbances might be solar prominences — great streams of hot hydrogen gas that extend tens or hundreds of thousands of miles beyond the sun. Or the spots may indicate locations where solar flares have occurred earlier. A flare occurs when a small area of the sun becomes extremely bright and hot and when particles from the sun are ejected into space. Some of these particles may enter earth's upper atmosphere, where they cause reactions that produce the auroras — or the northern and southern lights.

Sunspots will not appear very large, for the entire sun appears to be only about ½° from side to side. (This means that 360 suns could be placed in a line between the eastern and western horizons.)

Total eclipses of the sun are exciting events that can be observed readily by the amateur with equipment no more elaborate than a piece of smoked glass. Total solar eclipses visible from some part of North America up to and including 1991 are listed in the following table:

1959, October 2	*Eastern New England*
1970, March 7	*Mexico, Florida*
1972, July 10	*Alaska, Northern Canada*
1979, February 26	*Northwest United States, Canada*
1984, May 30	*Mexico, Southern United States*
1991, July 11	*Mexico, Central America*

At the time of an eclipse, local newspapers carry information about the exact moment the eclipse begins, the time of mid-eclipse, and the time it ends.

A solar eclipse occurs during a new-moon phase, when the moon is between the earth and the sun. The lighted half of the moon is turned away from the earth, and the moon is completely invisible. The moon moves faster than the sun, and so the moon overtakes the sun. It moves in front of it, blocking the sun from view. The dark region that appears on the sun as the eclipse begins is actually the edge of the moon. When the eclipse is complete, the black region is actually the dark half of the moon. It is in a direct line between us and the sun and so cuts off the sunlight.

During an eclipse, phenomena of the sun visible at no other time become apparent to the observer on earth. For example, just before totality is reached, when the moon covers the disk of the sun completely, a string of bright lights appear along the edge of the moon. They are called Baily's beads after Francis Baily, an English astronomer who described them after his viewing of the eclipse that occurred May 15, 1836. They are produced when sunlight still shines through the deep valleys at the lunar edge and so produces the string of disconnected lights.

Also, during a total eclipse the observer can see the corona, the crownlike formation that surrounds the sun. It does not extend as far at all points along the edge; some areas are considerably narrower than others, probably an effect of the sun's magnetic field. During totality it is sometimes possible to see solar prominences, tremendous flows of hot hydrogen gas that have been known to extend a million miles beyond the surface of the sun.

During eclipses, scientists measure the amount of decrease in light intensity by using light meters. A simple way for you to measure variations in light intensity is described below. Aim an ordinary photographic light meter at a reflecting surface. Record the reading. During the eclipse, make additional readings while holding the meter in the identical position. A comparison of the two readings gives a mathematical evaluation of the decrease in light intensity.

There are many facts that you can learn about the sun at times other than during eclipses. For example, you can measure the diameter of the sun.

SOLAR DIAMETER

You can find the diameter of the sun by following these directions. Pull down a shade that faces toward the south and put a pin hole through it. If you have no shades, cover the window with paper that light does not pass through easily (wrapping paper, for example). The hole should be located so the light that passes through it makes a spot of light on a chair. Place a cardboard on the chair so that the card is at right angles to the beam of light.

Draw a line tangent to the top of the spot and another line parallel to the first and tangent to the bottom of the spot. Carefully measure the distance between the lines. Suppose that you find the distance to be 1¼ inches.

Now measure the distance from the white cardboard to the hole in the shade. Suppose this distance is 132 inches.

You now have enough information to find the diameter of the sun: you have the diameter of the image (1¼ inches), the distance to the shade (132 inches), and the distance to the sun (93,000,000 miles). The following proportion will enable you to determine the diameter of the sun:

$$1.25 \quad : \quad 132 \quad :: \quad X \quad : \quad 93{,}000{,}000$$
$$132\,X = 116{,}250{,}000$$
$$X = 880{,}681$$

According to our computation, the sun is 880,681 miles in diameter. This is a good result, for the diameter determined by precise methods is 864,000 miles.

The sun is our daytime star. Interestingly enough, we have never seen the sun as it is at any particular moment. When we look at it, we see the sun as it was eight minutes ago, for it takes eight minutes for sunlight to travel the 93,000,000 miles between earth and sun. We say that the sun is eight light minutes from earth.

Sometimes the rising or setting sun appears flattened at both top and bottom; at other times the flattening effect occurs only at the bottom. In either case, earth's atmosphere is the cause. The effect is usually more noticeable at sunset.

When the sun is setting, the light is bent by earth's atmosphere. Light from the base of the sun passes through denser atmosphere which contains more dust particles than the upper atmosphere. The light from the lower part of the sun is therefore refracted, or bent,

more than light from the upper part of the sun. This causes the sun to appear misshapen.

TELLING TIME

As you view the sun from the United States, it is always in the south at noontime, east of south in the morning, and west of south in the afternoon. The changing position of the sun is not caused by movement of the sun itself. The changes are apparent: they result because the earth is spinning on its axis; it is rotating. Since we know the general position of the sun at different times, we can find directions by using a watch and the sun. This procedure can be used whenever the sun is shining.

Hold a watch in the palm of your hand, and turn it so the hour hand points toward the sun. South will be halfway between the hour hand and the number 12 on the dial. For example, if 3 on the dial is toward the sun, then south is halfway between 1 and 2. East is left of that position, west is right, and north directly opposite.

It is quite apparent from this and from other observations that the sun changes location in the sky throughout the day, rising toward the east and setting toward the west. The changing position of the sun in the sky can be used to tell time by using a sundial. You can make one that determines time quite accurately. Sundials can be designed in a variety of ways. You will find that the one explained below works very well. Since it is made of cardboard, it will not last long if you leave it outside. It may be waterproofed by spraying it with plastic. However, once you have made this one, you may want to make a more durable sundial from wood or metal.

Find the center of an 8-by-8-inch square of cardboard by drawing two diagonals. Place a compass at the intersection and draw a large circle on the cardboard. Divide half of the circle into twelve divisions as indicated, labeling them in order from 6 to 12 and from

1 to 6. With a safety-razor blade, cut a slit ½ inch from the center to within one inch of the outside of the circle. This is the base of the sundial. The slit is to support the upright, called the gnomon, a word that comes from the Greek word meaning "one that knows."

The gnomon is made as follows: Cut a piece of cardboard the length of which is equal to the radius of the circle. Cut a lip ¼ inch deep and as long as the slit made in the base. Fashion the gnomon somewhat as indicated in the drawing. The angle should be equal to your latitude. The latitude of New York, for instance, is 41°, Los Angeles 34°, Chicago 42°, Denver 40°. You can find the latitude of your place in an atlas. Insert the lip or tab of the gnomon in the base, and your sundial is ready to be used.

Take the instrument outside and place it on a sturdy platform in full sunlight. The 12 on the dial should line up with geographic north. You can be sure that the position of your sundial is correct if, at noontime (standard time), the gnomon casts no shadow; the sun is due south at noontime. You can also determine direction by using a watch dial as explained earlier. The gnomon should point toward Polaris (North Star), which is very near to true north. You can line up the gnomon at night by sighting along the upper edge.

A magnetic compass could be used to determine north; however, if you do use a compass, you must correct your readings for magnetic declination at many locations. Magnetic north and true north do not coincide at all places. At New York City true north is 11° east of magnetic north; at Los Angeles it is 15° west of magnetic north; at Chicago, 1° west, and so on. You can find the declination for your home region in the *World Almanac*. Once the sundial is set up properly, it should not be moved.

Another type of sundial can be made as follows. Obtain two circles of cardboard, each 6 inches in diameter. Mark on each card the scales indicated in the illustration. Cut out several cardboard circles and paste them together to make a sturdy disk, or cut a 6-inch wooden disk. Glue the two dials to the heavy disk, being sure that

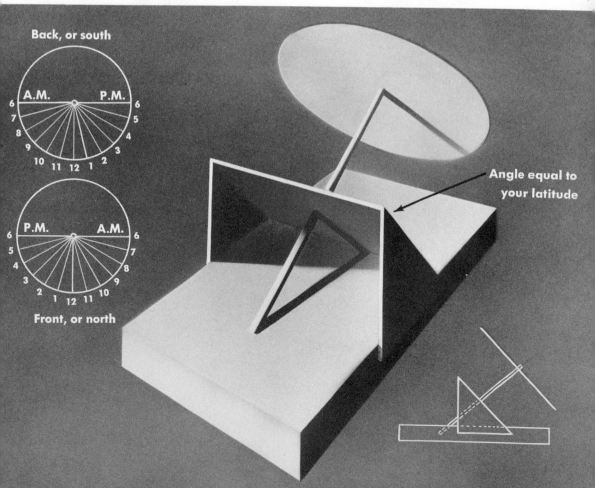

Back, or south

A.M.   P.M.
6   6
7   5
8   4
9   3
10 11 12 1 2

P.M.   A.M.
6   6
5   7
4   8
3   9
2 1 12 11 10

Front, or north

Angle equal to your latitude

the lines coincide. Drill a small hole through the center of the disk and insert a ¼-inch dowel through the hole.

Now you need a support for the dial. Cut a 6-inch square of wood and two wooden triangles. The angle of the slant of the triangle should equal your latitude. Fasten the triangles to the wooden base as shown and then connect them with another board. Drill a hole through the center of this board and insert the dowel through the hole. Push the dowel through until it hits the base. Fasten the dowel to the base with a small nail or a slender screw.

You use this sundial the same way that you used the one above. Point the gnomon, the dowel, toward the north. During summer, when the sun is quite far north, the shadow of the dowel falls on the front of the dial. Make your reading there. During winter, when the sun is farther south, the shadow falls on the back of the dial.

When the sun is shining, the shadow of the gnomon indicates the time of day. The time is standard; so, if you are on daylight saving time, you must add one hour to the reading. Standard time was put into effect about a hundred years ago. Before then, a place a few miles away from a particular location might have had a different time. This caused great confusion, especially for those people who were trying to keep trains on schedule. When standard time is used, a region several hundred miles wide has the same time throughout. This means that people who travel need not adjust their watches either forward or backward to the time of another city except when they move from one standard time zone (or region) to another one. Daylight saving time is determined in the same way. However, daylight saving time is pushed ahead one hour: if it is 10 o'clock standard time, it would be 11 o'clock daylight time.

Because the sun is not a single point of light, the shadow cast by the gnomon is fuzzy. Therefore, the readings cannot be made with precise accuracy. There are other reasons why time as indicated by the sundial will not agree with clock time.

Time indicated by a sundial is local solar time, not average, or mean, solar time. Earth does not always move at the same speed around the sun; it moves faster in January, for example, than it does in July. To avoid the variations in the length of the day that result, we use an imaginary sun that is assumed to move always at the same speed. This imaginary sun gives us mean solar time. Mean solar time and local solar time may vary by as much as 16 minutes throughout the year. When reading time on your sundial, refer to the equation of time chart shown here to see how many minutes you must add to or subtract from the actual reading on your sundial to make it agree with clock time.

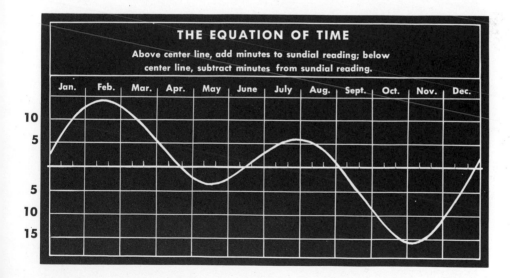

Perhaps you have noticed on certain globes of the earth what appears at first to be a figure 8. The figure usually is drawn in the Pacific Ocean somewhere on the equator, simply because there is a blank space in that region. The figure 8 is called an analemma, after the Greek word for "sundial." It represents the difference between clock time (or mean solar time) and the position of the sun relative to your meridian throughout the year.

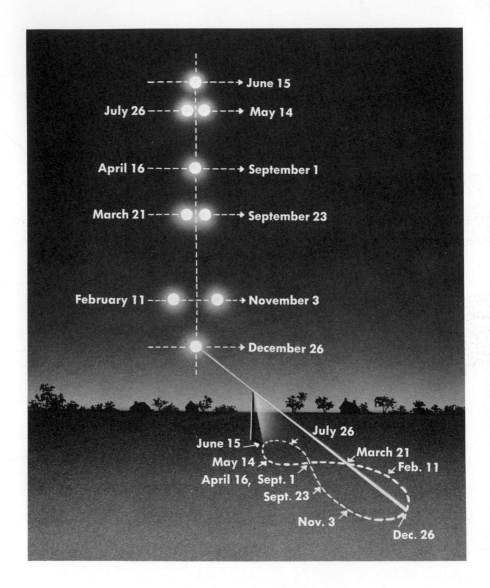

The diagram shows how and why the figure 8 is obtained. Suppose you were to draw a line on the sky for your meridian, due north and south. At noontime the sun should be on that meridian. But it is not every day throughout the year. The only times the real sun is on the meridian at noontime are around April 16, June 15,

September 1, and December 26. During January through March, noontime occurs before the sun reaches the meridian. In May, noontime occurs after the sun has passed the meridian. In July, noontime again occurs before the sun has reached the meridian. And then from September through December the sun is past the meridian at noontime. Notice also that the summer sun (indicated by the June 15 position) is high in the sky compared to the winter sun (indicated by the December 26 position). When the various positions occupied by the noontime sun in the course of a year are joined together, an analemma results.

Your longitude also may cause the reading of the sundial to differ from clock time. Your watch gives standard time, and all places within a given time zone have the same time. Each zone covers about 15 degrees of longitude, 7.5 degrees east and west of a given meridian. For example, New York City is in the Eastern Standard time zone. The meridian for the zone is the 75th.

A sundial in New York City will be 4 minutes ahead of a watch because the longitude of New York City is 74° — the sun is overhead there 4 minutes before it is overhead for someone on the 75th meridian. Therefore, 4 minutes must be subtracted from the sundial reading to make it agree with watch time. Four minutes must be subtracted from the sundial for every degree east of the meridian. Four minutes must be added to the sundial reading for every degree you are west of the meridian of your time zone. This is because the sun has not reached your location. The meridians in the United States and Canada that are at the approximate centers of the time zones are at longitudes 60, 75, 90, 105, 120, 135.

The discoveries you have made about the sun indicate the many changes that occur continually in this nearest star of ours. The discoveries will become more significant if you write them up, giving important details, so you may have your personal science notebook.

THE MOON

3

To sky watchers of long ago, the moon was of considerable importance, for it enabled men to determine the beginning of the month. The first appearance of the new crescent moon in the western sky told them a new month was beginning.

Check your calendar to find the date of the next new moon. During this phase, the moon is between the sun and the earth. The lighted half of the moon is away from the earth, and so the new moon is completely invisible. However, a night or so after new moon you should be able to see the first thin crescent in the western sky right after sunset. The new crescent moon sets an hour or so after sunset. The setting of the sun or moon, or any other celestial object, occurs when the object disappears below the horizon.

On each succeeding night, the moon appears higher in the western sky at sunset. Also, with each succeeding night, we see more of the moon surface. After one week, the moon is in the first quarter phase, and it is almost due south at sunset. It sets about six hours after sunset.

Two weeks after the first appearance of the slim crescent in the west, the moon rises out of the east as the sun sets. Now the moon is full.

The third quarter moon and the last crescent moon rise after midnight; they are not visible in the evening sky.

People of long ago used the interval between two successive appearances of a crescent moon in the evening sky as a measure of time; they called it the month. Today, the month is still an important time division, although we do not usually use the cycle of moon phases for determining the month.

You may have heard that we always see the same half of the moon; the other half is always turned away from us. This is essentially true. Actually, we see a little more than half of the moon.

Some people believe that we see the same half of the moon because the moon does not rotate. But the moon *must* rotate in order for the other half to be away from earth constantly. You can prove this to yourself. Place a chair in the center of a room; the chair represents the earth. You represent the moon. Stand facing the chair. Move around the chair, facing the same wall constantly. The moon moved around the earth, it revolved. But the moon did not rotate, therefore all parts of the moon were turned toward earth. Now move around the chair, facing the chair at all times. The moon revolved around the chair once, and the moon rotated once; therefore, only one side of the moon was toward earth.

Very likely the moon used to rotate much faster than it does now. Earth's gravitational attraction has caused tides on the moon. One effect of these tides has been to slow down the speed of rotation. The rotation speed is so slow, about 10 miles per hour, that the moon appears to observers on earth as though it were not turning at all. A similar relationship exists between Mercury and the sun. This small planet moves around the sun in 88 days and it rotates once in 88 days; therefore, the same side of Mercury is always toward the sun. We believe that the four principal satellites of Jupiter have been affected by the gravitational attraction of the mother planet so that each of them keeps the same side toward the planet at all times.

Sky watchers can see a little more than half of the moon when they make their observations over a considerable length of time. There are many reasons why we can see more than 50 per cent of the moon. All of the reasons together are called the moon's libration (from *libra*, which means "to balance").

The first reason has to do with the speed of the moon's revolution. The moon does not always revolve around the earth at the same speed. It moves in a manner that Johannes Kepler, the German astronomer, computed some three hundred years ago. Kepler's statements or laws were formulated for orbits of planets around the sun. But the same reasoning applies to the moon and earth. Kepler said that the moon revolves so that an imaginary line joining the

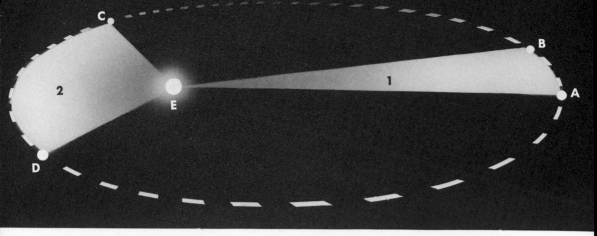

moon to the earth sweeps over equal areas in equal intervals of time.
Let us see what this means.

When the moon is near the earth, it revolves much faster than
when it is farther away. The diagram shows that the orbit of the
moon about the earth is elliptical. (Actually the path is much more
nearly circular. We have exaggerated the flatness of the ellipse.)
Suppose one day is required for the moon to move from *A* to *B*.
During that day, a line (*AE*) from the moon to earth would sweep
out the area marked 1. During any other day, twelve days later, for
example, a line from earth to moon must sweep out the exact same
area; the moon must move from *C* to *D* to sweep out the area
marked 2. Area 2 equals area 1. The distance from *A* to *B* is much
less than the distance from *C* to *D*, yet the moon requires only one
day to move from *A* to *B*, or from *C* to *D*. Because the distance
C to *D* is greater than the distance *A* to *B*, the moon must move
much faster when it is in this part of the orbit.

Usually the moon makes a quarter of a rotation while moving a
quarter of the way around the earth. The next diagram shows that,
when the moon is revolving fast, it goes slightly more than a quarter
of the way around the earth while making one quarter of a rotation.
This enables us to see slightly around it. Similarly, when the moon
is revolving slowly, it goes slightly less than a quarter of the way
around the earth while making one rotation. Therefore, we see

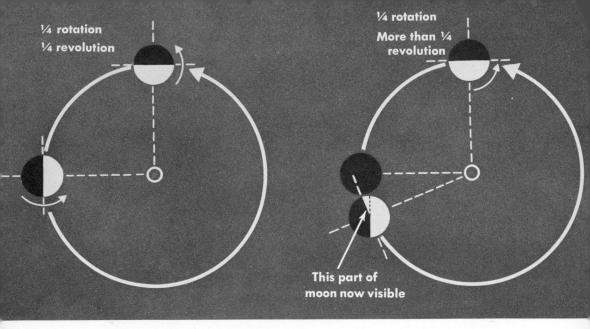

¼ rotation
¼ revolution

¼ rotation
More than ¼
revolution

This part of
moon now visible

slightly around the other side of the moon. This is libration in longitude — libration from side to side.

The axis of rotation of the moon is tilted 6°.5 from a line perpendicular to its orbit. Therefore, at one time we see 6°.5 beyond one of the poles, and half a month later we see the same distance beyond the other pole. We look down upon the moon at one time, you might say, and we look up at the moon two weeks later. This is called libration in latitude — libration up and down.

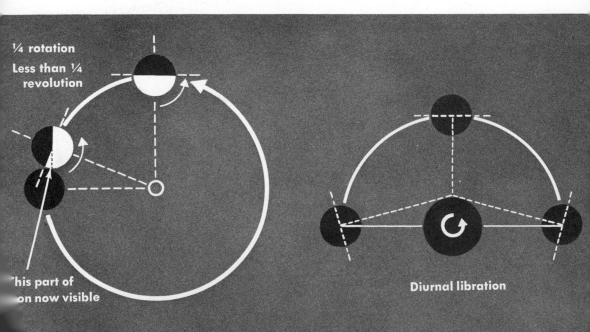

¼ rotation
Less than ¼
revolution

This part of
moon now visible

Diurnal libration

A third cause of libration is shown in the diagram. At moonrise the observer can look slightly over the upper edge of the moon and so he can see a little more of that part of the moon than he can see at any other time. By moonset, some 12 hours later, he once more can look slightly over the other edge of the moon. This is called diurnal (daily) libration.

These librations make it possible to see 59 per cent of the surface of the moon. Forty-one per cent of the surface can be seen at all times when the phase permits, and 18 per cent can be observed at some times but not at others. Earthmen have never seen 41 per cent of the surface of the moon.

Very likely the other side of the moon is not different from the side we already know. However, to find out for certain, we shall have to wait until man reaches the moon in a space ship. Or perhaps a drone ship equipped with television will explore the other side of the moon and send to earth sharp, detailed pictures which will enable us to construct a map of it.

We will then be able to set at ease the mind of the housemaid who wrote these lines some time ago:

> *O moon, lovely moon with the beautiful face,*
> *Careering throughout the bound'ries of space,*
> *Whenever I see you, I think on my mind —*
> *Shall I ever, oh ever, behold thy behind?*

LUNAR ECLIPSE

An eclipse of the moon is not as spectacular as a solar eclipse; however, a lunar eclipse can be observed readily by the amateur.

A lunar eclipse occurs when the moon moves into earth's shadow. This can occur quite frequently because the shadow of the earth is about 857,000 miles long and, at the distance of the moon, it is about 5,690 miles in diameter. Because of the large

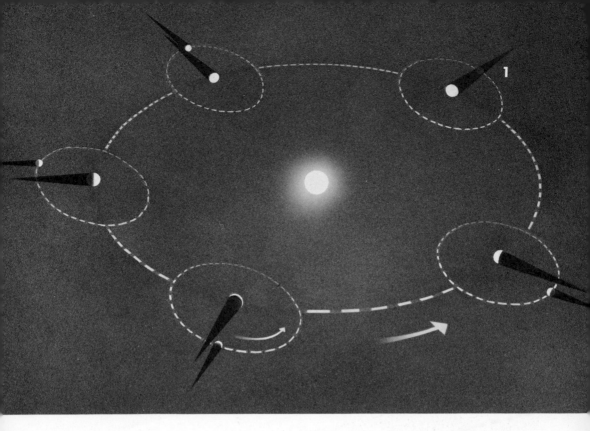

diameter of earth's shadow — more than twice the moon's diameter of 2,160 miles — the entire moon enters the shadow. As a result, people on all parts of the earth that is in full moonlight can see the total lunar eclipse. This is quite different from a solar eclipse. Here the shadow of the moon is so narrow that a strip of the earth only about 69 miles wide can experience totality.

Earth is between the sun and moon once every month — during each full moon. In other words, the three bodies are in positions that could produce a lunar eclipse. Yet, we do not experience a lunar eclipse each month. An eclipse occurs only when the moon moves into earth's shadow. This cannot happen each month because the plane of the moon's path is tilted to the plane of the earth's path. The diagram shows the sun, earth, and moon during full moon at different times of the year. A lunar eclipse occurs only at position 1.

Lunar eclipses visible in the United States from 1960 through 1972 are listed in the table here.

		All of U.S.	*Part of U.S.*
1960	March 13	"	
1960	September 5		"
1961	March 2		"
1961	August 26		"
1963	December 30		"
1964	June 25		"
1965	June 14		"
1967	April 24		"
1967	October 18		"
1968	April 13	"	
1970	August 17	"	
1971	February 10	"	
1971	August 6	"	
1972	January 30	"	

The shadow of an object is made of two sections. The lighter part of the shadow is called the penumbra, and the darker portion is called the umbra.

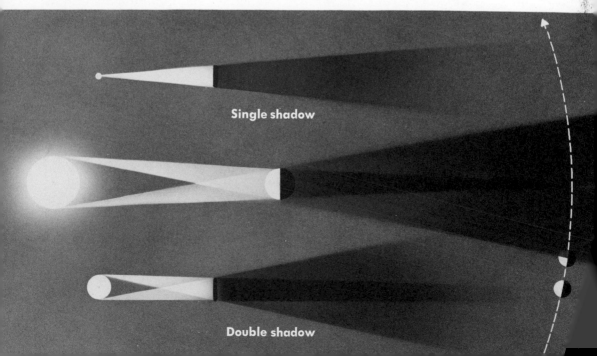

Single shadow

Double shadow

It is quite impossible to tell when the moon enters the lighter portion (penumbra) of earth's shadow, because the decrease in brightness is so slight. However, if you observe the eclipse carefully, you will be able to see a decrease in brightness just before the moon enters the umbra of the shadow. After a few moments, a small dark area with a curved boundary notches the eastern edge of the moon. This is the umbra of earth's shadow. The shadow obscures more and more of the moon until, after about one hour, it is entirely within the earth's dark shadow; the moon is in total eclipse. It is still visible, though ruddy and dim. This is because light is bent as it passes through our atmosphere. The violet, blue, and green parts of sunlight are bent very much. However, this light is scattered by water vapor in our atmosphere and so it does not reach the moon. The reds and oranges are bent also, although not so much as the violets, and they pass through our atmosphere. The red light enters the shadow of the earth and so falls upon the moon. As a result, we see a ruddy, coppery moon during the eclipse rather than a totally dark moon.

Conditions in our atmosphere change, so that sometimes all the colors of sunlight are cut off completely, and the moon cannot be seen at all during the eclipse. Such events are rare. The last such occasion was in 1884. As the moon moves out of earth's shadow, the observer sees all these happenings take place, but in reverse order.

SIZE OF THE MOON

The moon seems to be very large when it rises above the horizon, and it appears to grow smaller as it moves higher in the sky. But it is obvious that the moon does not change in size. In fact, it cannot. The changing size is an illusion. You can prove to yourself that the size does not change.

When full moon is near the horizon, look at it through a window.

Measure the distance between the window and your eyes. Put a strip of adhesive tape on the window along the top edge of the moon, and another strip along the bottom edge. Two hours later, when the moon is higher in the sky, stand in exactly the same place, the same distance from the window and again place strips of adhesive tape along the top and bottom edges of the moon. Measure the distance between the first pair of strips, and also between the second pair. They will be the same; the size of the moon did not change.

Another way of showing this is to make photographs of the moon at different times. We cannot tell you the speed or opening to use on your camera, for light conditions vary. We suggest that you try different exposure times and diaphragm stops to set up your own tables for best results. Photograph the full moon at different positions in the sky, and then measure the images carefully. Once more, you find that they are the same size.

You can also make rough measures with a stick. Hold a pencil or similar stick upright at arm's length. Wrap four fingers about it and hold the tip of your thumb against the stick. Measure the size of the moon by raising the stick until the top of the moon is touched by the end of the stick, and the bottom of the moon coincides with the tip of your thumb. Measure the length of the exposed stick with a ruler.

Perform the same operation later when the moon is higher in the sky. Once more, you find that the size of the moon has not changed at all.

THE MAN IN THE MOON

Imaginative observers have "seen" all manner of formations on the moon. Perhaps the form seen most frequently is the man in the moon.

The surface of the moon is covered with high mountains which cast deep shadows. The play of lights and shadows produces the illusion of various shapes and figures.

The moon contains many flat regions which are considerably darker than the mountains. Some astronomers believe that the flat areas are covered with dustlike deposits of small meteorites that have fallen on the moon and sifted into the lowlands. Light does not reflect well from these darker areas, and so a varation in light intensity results. Other astronomers believe that the darker areas of the moon are covered with a hard surface, strong enough to support men and their space ships. They agree with those who tell us that the moon is covered with dust, that meteorites, microscopic in size, rained onto the moon for billions of years. It is their opinion that the particles are so small that they have packed close together, and the high heat of the lunar surface (215° F. at noon) has caused the particles to fuse into a hard, plasticlike layer.

RING AROUND THE MOON OR SUN

There is a popular belief that a ring around the moon is a sign of rain. Some people even believe that the number of stars within the ring tells the number of days that will elapse before the rain falls. You might test this belief yourself to find whether or not it is true. Make a record of every sighting of the ring, count the number of stars within it, and note when the rain occurs. See if there is any connection between the appearance of the ring and the occurrence of rain. Did you find that the number of stars in the ring made any difference?

The ring around the moon is not astronomical in nature; it is caused by clouds in our own atmosphere. The clouds are six or seven miles high where the temperature is below freezing. Therefore, the clouds are composed of very small ice crystals. The ice crystals act as prisms, bending the light and often dispersing the white light into the various colors of which it is composed. The ice crystals are six-sided, or hexagonal. They act the same as 60° glass prisms. When sunlight strikes such a prism, the white light is dispersed into the colors of which it is made — red, orange, yellow, green, blue, and violet — the colors of the rainbow.

We do not see the colors distinctly in a ring around the moon, although the more common ring is somewhat reddish on the inside. The colors merge into yellow, green, and blue as one looks toward the outside of the ring. Very often the colors are not apparent, or they are extremely faint, and so the sky watcher sees a nebulous, whitish ring. The manner in which the ring forms is shown in the illustration.

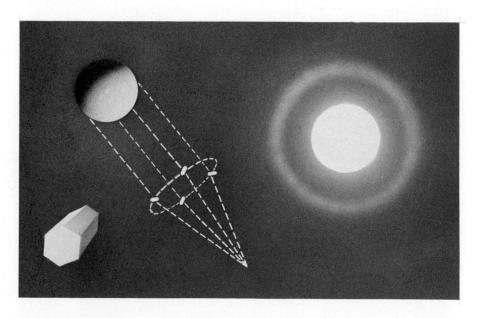

When rings form around the moon or sun, there are usually two of them. The first will have a radius of 22° and the second will have a radius of 46°. That is, a line drawn from the center of the moon (or sun) to your eye would make a 22° angle with a line drawn from your eye to the inner ring and a 46° angle with a line drawn from your eye to the outer ring.

You can measure the angles roughly in the following manner. Point directly at the sun or moon with your index finger. (CAU-TION: If you look directly at the sun use a piece of smoked glass as explained in chapter 2.) Then move your middle finger until it points at the ring. Measure the angle at the junction of the two fingers with a protractor.

Make a more accurate measuring device by connecting two pieces of cardboard 12 by 2 inches with a brass paper fastener. Sight the sun or moon along the top edge of one of the strips. While holding the first strip steady, sight the ring along the bottom edge of the second strip. Measure the angle at the intersection of the two strips with a protractor.

At the same time that the ring is seen, a faint white line may appear to pass directly through the moon or sun parallel to the horizon and to continue out beyond the rings. This line extended all around the sky is called the parhelic circle. Where the line inter-sects the rings or halos that surround the moon, the halo becomes more intense. The observer sees what appears to be an image of the

moon; this is a moon dog. Sometimes several such images are present. Sometimes the images can be seen, but the halos or rings are invisible, making a very impressive sight indeed.

THE HARVEST MOON

A full moon around the time of the beginning of autumn is called a harvest moon. At this time the moon may rise only about 15 minutes later each night instead of the usual 50 minutes. The phrase had its beginnings in early England and is so called because farmers can harvest their crops late into the evening by the light of the full moon, and the moon will shine for many nights.

In order to understand why there is a harvest moon, we must have some knowledge of the meaning of culmination. Directly over your head, and running from north to south, is the imaginary line called your meridian. Whenever a celestial object crosses that meridian at any point, we say that it culminates; the event is a culmination.

The moon moves rapidly toward the east in its passage around the earth. Because of this rapid motion, the moon culminates — crosses the meridian — 51 minutes later each day, or night, as the case may be. Also, the moon rises and sets about 50 minutes later each night. However, occasionally the time of the rising and setting of the nearly full moon varies by more than 50 minutes from one day to another. At other times the variation is considerably less. In fact, around the beginning of autumn, the delay in the rising of the moon may be as little as 15 minutes from one night to its rising the next.

We suggest that you record the time of moonrise for a while and make a tabulation similar to the one below, which shows the retardation of moonrise for part of September 1958. Note that the interval grows much less around the time of the fall equinox, the last week of September.

Date	Moonrise	Daily Retardation (*minutes*)	Moon Phase
September 13	12:45		New moon
14	1:55	70	
15	3:05	70	
16	4:14	69	
17	5:22	68	
18	6:26	64	
19	7:25	59	First quarter
20	8:19	54	
21	9:07	48	
22	9:50	43	
23	10:29	39	
24	11:05	36	
25	11:38	33	
26	12:10	32	
27	12:41	31	Full moon
28	1:13	32	
29	1:46	33	
30	2:22	36	

To understand why the retardation in moonrise decreases in the autumn, you must know the positions of both the sun and the moon at that season. Also, you must understand the relation between the celestial equator, the ecliptic, and the horizon.

Imagine that the sky is two great bowls inverted over the earth. When you look into the sky, you are looking into the inside of one bowl.

If you look straight overhead, you are looking at your zenith. If you could look in the opposite direction, through the center of the earth and to the opposite sky, you would be looking at your nadir.

The edge of the bowl that is all around you is your horizon.

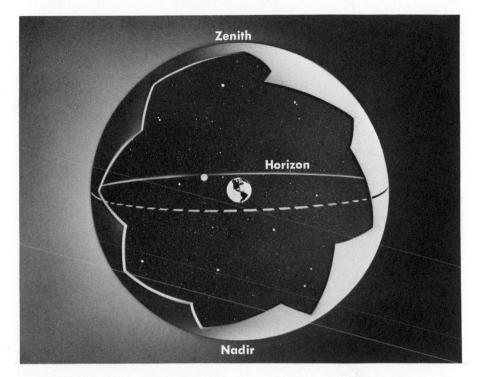

The equator is an imaginary line going around the earth midway between the North and South Poles. If you extend the equator of the earth out to the sky, you have another imaginary line; this is called the equator of the sky, or the celestial equator (see page 40).

The ecliptic is the path that the sun appears to follow through the sky in the course of one year. In reality, earth revolves around the sun, and so we see the sun in different parts of the sky. You can get an idea how this works by moving around a chair in the center of a room. The chair is the sun, and you are the earth. The walls represent the sky. As you change position, the chair appears to be against different walls. Similarly, as earth changes position, the sun would appear to be among different stars if the stars were visible. When we join together the various locations that the sun appears to occupy throughout a year, we have the ecliptic.

The moon appears to follow the ecliptic in a general way. The relative positions of the ecliptic, the celestial equator, and the horizon change from spring to autumn.

In spring (see the diagram) the ecliptic (apparent path of the moon) meets the horizon at a steep angle. Looking toward the east, you would see the moon rise as the horizon moved from 1, the position of the moon the previous moonrise, to position 2. This change is a result of the moon's traveling eastward along its orbit during the 24-hour interval. During the night and the next day, the moon would move from position 2 to 4. The next night, the turning of the earth would cause the moon to rise at position 4. The line 3—4, which parallels the celestial equator, indicates the motion of the horizon. The difference in length between lines 1—2 and 3—4

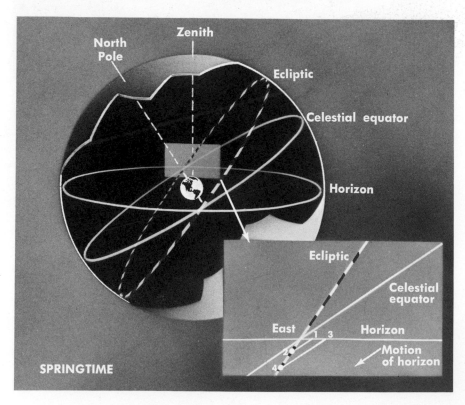

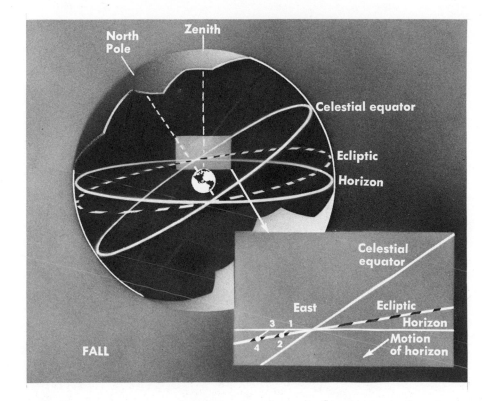

indicates how much later the moon would rise. The line 3–4 is much longer, therefore moonrise would occur much later.

In the fall, at the time of the harvest moon, the ecliptic meets the horizon at a smaller angle than it did in springtime (see the diagram). In 24 hours the moon moves from 2 to 4 on the ecliptic. The line 1–2 shows the way the horizon moves from the position of moonrise the previous night (1) to the next moonrise (2). The line 3–4 is a bit longer than line 1–2. This means that moonrise is a bit later each night, but only a few minutes later.

Keep records of the time of moonrise and moonset throughout the year. Compile your own proof that there are large variations between the risings in springtime and those that occur around the time that fall begins.

THE PLANETS

4

PEOPLE WHO lived long ago watched the stars with great care. In fact, astronomy in the days before the telescope and camera consisted entirely of sky study with the naked eye. Long ago observers noticed that the vast majority of the stars remained in the same positions relative to each other. However, certain stars changed position in the sky from week to week, and from month to month. Indeed, there were times when they could not be seen at all. Because they changed position in the sky, these stars were called wanderers by the ancients. The Greek word for wanderer gave us *planet*, the word by which we know these "stars" today.

Before the telescope was invented, men knew of five wandering stars, or planets. These were Mercury, Venus, Mars, Jupiter, and Saturn, the five planets that are bright enough to be seen with the unaided eye. We now believe that there are nine planets. These are the five mentioned above, plus Earth, Uranus, Neptune, and Pluto. Uranus, Neptune, and Pluto cannot be seen very well, even with a moderate-sized telescope, because they are not very bright.

Planets do not produce light; they reflect sunlight to us, and so they must be close to us or very large to be seen. Therefore, even though all planets are much closer to earth than stars, only Mars, Venus, Jupiter, and Saturn can be seen easily. The planet farthest from us is Pluto — about 3,000 million miles away. But the nearest star, Proxima Centauri, is much farther away, about 26 million million miles, yet we can see it more easily.

Other stars may have planets moving about them, but we have no way of finding out whether this is true or not. Only by using a powerful telescope can we see the outermost planets that are moving about our own star; it is absolutely impossible to see planets that may be moving about more distant stars.

Today we can understand why planets appear to wander among the stars, because we know that planets are close by, while stars are very distant. The diagram shows why this happens. Earth and Mars are used as examples. Imagine that you are observing Mars while earth and Mars are in the positions numbered 1. Mars would appear to be among certain stars. Later on, the two planets would have moved in their orbits; they would be in different positions, positions numbered 2, let us say. Now Mars would appear to be among different stars.

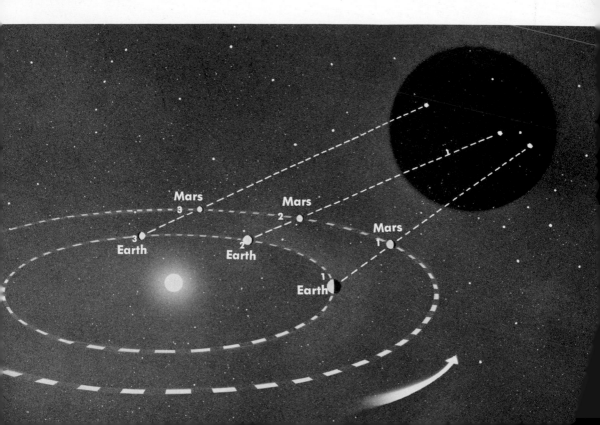

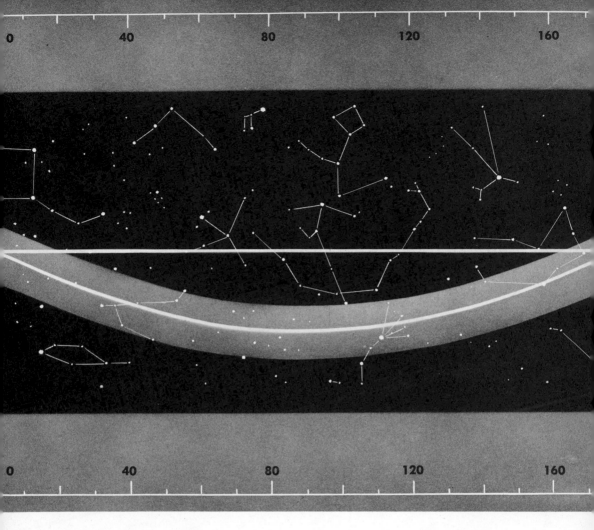

If you notice that a "star" changes its position among the stars, you can be sure you are observing a planet. The two planets you will see most frequently are Mars and Venus because they often are bright in the early evening. Mercury is very small and close to the sun and cannot be seen very well. Jupiter and Saturn can be seen with the naked eye; but, because of their distance from us, they never reach the maximum brightness of Venus.

Mars appears very bright indeed at times, and it also has a reddish color. Some astronomers believe that the color is caused by red dust that has formed on the surface. They say that the dust is

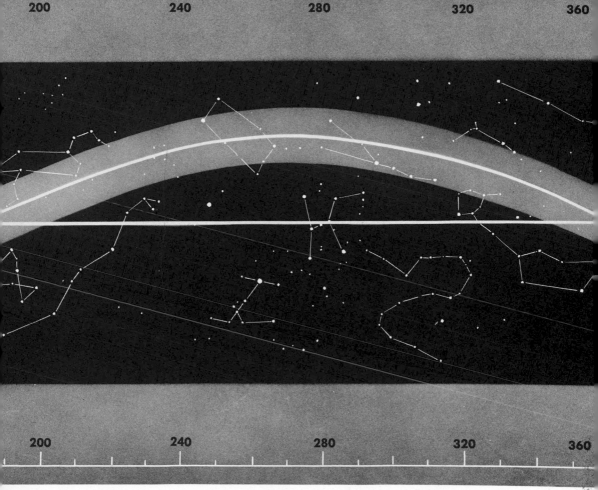

made of oxides of metals, such as iron oxide (rust), for example.

Venus can be the brightest of all the planets. Sometimes it is so bright that we can see it in our daytime sky. At such times only the sun and moon exceed Venus in brightness.

The planets revolve around the sun; therefore we always see them in nearly the same plane with the sun — near the ecliptic. But, because of the earth's tilt, the angle at which we look at this plane at night is opposite to the day angle. When the ecliptic during the day is high, the ecliptic at night is low.

In order to know *when* to look for planets, refer to the tabulation given on pages 46—51. This tells you when the planet can be seen — whether morning or evening and the best occasions for making observations.

POSITIONS OF THE PLANETS FROM 1959 TO 1969

The curved line on pages 44—45 is the ecliptic, near which the planets always appear. Mercury is never beyond 6° of it, Venus and Mars are never beyond 7° of it, Jupiter 2°, and Saturn 3°.

The numbers in the tables give the positions along the ecliptic. The bold numbers indicate that the planet is visible in the evening; the lighter numbers indicate that it is visible in the early morning. Locate the number on the star chart, and this will give you the nearby constellation in which the planet will appear. Information about the constellations is in the chapter on stars.

All positions are for the 13th of the month. If you wish the position for an earlier part of the month, look to the west (the right). If you wish it for a later part of the month, look to the east (the left).

Example: Suppose you wish to observe Venus in September 1960. Opposite September 1960 you find that Venus will be at 194° in the evening. This position on the ecliptic (194°) is a bit west of Virgo, and north of Corvus. That is the place in the sky to look for Venus at that time.

1959

ALL POSITIONS ARE FOR THE 13TH OF THE MONTH.

	Mercury	Venus	Mars	Jupiter	Saturn
JULY	**136**	**154**	**146**	**233**	**272**
AUGUST		**166**	**166**	**233**	**271**
SEPTEMBER			**185**	**237**	**270**
OCTOBER		158		**242**	**272**
NOVEMBER	**250**	184	226		**274**
DECEMBER	240	217	247	255	

1960

ALL POSITIONS ARE FOR THE 13TH OF THE MONTH.

	Mercury	Venus	Mars	Jupiter	Saturn
JANUARY		254	270	262	281
FEBRUARY		292	293	268	284
MARCH		328	315	272	287
APRIL	357		339	274	288
MAY			2	273	288
JUNE	**107**		25	270	287
JULY			47	**266**	**285**
AUGUST			68	**264**	**282**
SEPTEMBER		**194**	86	**265**	**282**
OCTOBER	**225**	**231**	100	**268**	**282**
NOVEMBER		**268**	108	**274**	**284**
DECEMBER		**305**	105		

1961

ALL POSITIONS ARE FOR THE 13TH OF THE MONTH.

	Mercury	Venus	Mars	Jupiter	Saturn
JANUARY		**340**	**94**	287	291
FEBRUARY		**11**	**90**	294	294
MARCH	327	**29**	**96**	300	297
APRIL			**109**	305	299
MAY		15	**124**	307	300
JUNE		37	**141**	307	299
JULY		67	**159**	304	297
AUGUST		102	**178**	300	**294**
SEPTEMBER	**193**	138	**198**	298	**293**
OCTOBER		175	**218**	298	**293**
NOVEMBER			**240**	302	**295**
DECEMBER				307	298

1962

ALL POSITIONS ARE FOR THE 13TH OF THE MONTH.

	Mercury	*Venus*	*Mars*	*Jupiter*	*Saturn*
JANUARY			286		
FEBRUARY			310	321	305
MARCH	328		331	328	308
APRIL			356	334	310
MAY	**74**	**79**	18	339	311
JUNE		**116**	42	342	311
JULY		**151**	64	342	309
AUGUST		**186**	85	340	**307**
SEPTEMBER	**197**	**216**	104	**336**	**305**
OCTOBER		**236**	121	**333**	**304**
NOVEMBER			136	**333**	306
DECEMBER		225	144	**336**	**308**

1963

ALL POSITIONS ARE FOR THE 13TH OF THE MONTH.

	Mercury	*Venus*	*Mars*	*Jupiter*	*Saturn*
JANUARY		247	142	**342**	
FEBRUARY	299	279	**131**	**348**	315
MARCH		311	**125**		318
APRIL		348	**130**	2	321
MAY		24	**140**	9	323
JUNE	59	62	**155**	15	323
JULY			**172**	18	322
AUGUST	**166**		**191**	19	**320**
SEPTEMBER			**211**	17	**317**
OCTOBER			**232**	14	**316**
NOVEMBER			**254**	10	317
DECEMBER	**281**	**288**	277	10	319

1964

ALL POSITIONS ARE FOR THE 13TH OF THE MONTH.

	Mercury	Venus	Mars	Jupiter	Saturn
JANUARY		**326**	**300**	**12**	**322**
FEBRUARY	305	**4**		**17**	
MARCH		**37**	348	**23**	328
APRIL		**70**	12		332
MAY	32	**93**	35	38	334
JUNE			58	45	335
JULY		81	78	50	334
AUGUST	**167**	97	100	55	332
SEPTEMBER	164	126	119	56	**330**
OCTOBER		160	137	55	**328**
NOVEMBER		197	154	**51**	**327**
DECEMBER		234	168	**47**	**329**

1965

ALL POSITIONS ARE FOR THE 13TH OF THE MONTH.

	Mercury	Venus	Mars	Jupiter	Saturn
JANUARY	272	272	177	**46**	**332**
FEBRUARY			176	**48**	
MARCH			167	**52**	339
APRIL			159	**58**	343
MAY	28		162		345
JUNE			173	72	347
JULY	138	**136**	**188**	79	347
AUGUST		**173**	**206**	85	345
SEPTEMBER		**210**	**226**	90	**343**
OCTOBER		**245**	**247**	91	**341**
NOVEMBER	**254**	**279**	**270**	90	**340**
DECEMBER	243	**306**	**293**	87	**341**

1966

ALL POSITIONS ARE FOR THE 13TH OF THE MONTH.

	Mercury	*Venus*	*Mars*	*Jupiter*	*Saturn*
JANUARY			**317**	**83**	**343**
FEBRUARY		299	**342**	**81**	
MARCH		310	**4**	**82**	350
APRIL	357	337		**86**	354
MAY		10	49	**92**	357
JUNE		45	71		359
JULY	**132**	81	91	105	359
AUGUST	123	118	113	112	358
SEPTEMBER			132	118	356
OCTOBER	**221**		151	122	**353**
NOVEMBER			169	124	**353**
DECEMBER			185	124	**353**

1967

ALL POSITIONS ARE FOR THE 13TH OF THE MONTH.

	Mercury	*Venus*	*Mars*	*Jupiter*	*Saturn*
JANUARY			200	120	**355**
FEBRUARY	**342**	**348**	210	**116**	358
MARCH		**22**	213	**115**	
APRIL	9	**60**	205	**116**	5
MAY		**94**	**196**	**119**	8
JUNE	106	**128**	**197**	**124**	11
JULY		**154**	**208**		12
AUGUST		**163**	**223**	137	12
SEPTEMBER			**242**	144	10
OCTOBER	**225**	157	**263**	149	**8**
NOVEMBER	212	184	**286**	154	6
DECEMBER		218	**309**	156	5

1968

	Mercury	Venus	Mars	Jupiter	Saturn
JANUARY		255	**334**	155	**6**
FEBRUARY		292	**358**	152	**9**
MARCH	326	328	**20**	**148**	
APRIL			**42**	**146**	16
MAY			**64**	**147**	20
JUNE				**150**	23
JULY	91		105	**155**	25
AUGUST			125		25
SEPTEMBER	**197**	**194**	145	168	24
OCTOBER		**231**	164	174	22
NOVEMBER		**269**	183	180	**20**
DECEMBER		**305**	201	184	**18**

1969

	Mercury	Venus	Mars	Jupiter	Saturn
JANUARY	**313**	**340**	218	186	**19**
FEBRUARY	301	**11**	235	185	**21**
MARCH	342	**27**	247	182	**24**
APRIL			256	**178**	
MAY		14	255	**176**	31
JUNE		37	**245**	**177**	35
JULY		68	**242**	**180**	37
AUGUST	**162**	103	**250**	**185**	39
SEPTEMBER	**195**	139	**266**		38
OCTOBER	182	176	**285**	197	36
NOVEMBER			**307**	204	**34**
DECEMBER			**329**	210	**32**

MORNING AND EVENING "STARS"

Long ago people observed a brilliant star on certain evenings after sunset. After a few days, the star disappeared from the sky, and then a short time later they saw a bright star in the early morning before sunrise. They believed they were seeing two different stars. In fact, they called the evening star Hesperus, and they called the star that appeared just before the sun Phosphorus. Actually, these two objects were both the planet Venus.

Venus goes around the sun in an orbit between earth and sun. Sometimes Venus is west of a line joining earth and sun. We then see the planet in the morning; it is called a morning "star." Venus moves beyond the sun and we cannot see it. Then, a few weeks later, Venus is east of the sun, and we see it right after sunset; it is an evening "star." The planet continues on its way around the sun, and it occupies a position between us and the sun. Once more it is invisible.

The diagram shows the orbit of Venus and earth about the sun.

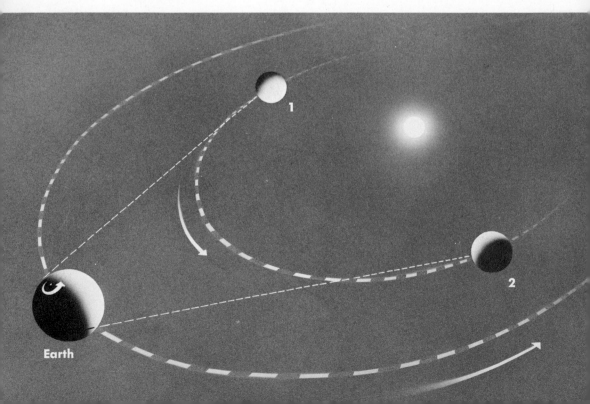

Earth

When Venus is at position 1, we can see the planet in the evening, just after sunset. When Venus is at position 2, we can see it an hour or so before sunrise. We cannot usually see Venus in daytime because the sky is too bright. Venus can never be seen by us at midnight because we are turned away from the planet at that time.

The experiment explained below will help you to understand why Venus is seen only at evening and at sunrise.

A table top is the surface of the earth. Label opposite sides of the table top east and west. Bend over so your eye is level with the table. Look toward the west — toward sunset. Have someone hold a flashlight even with the table top, so it lights a ball held in the person's other hand above the flashlight. The flashlight is the sun; the ball is Venus. Have him keep the flashlight on while moving it below the table top — the sun is setting. The light should be pointed at the ball — Venus. The planet is still above the horizon. The sun has set, but Venus is still visible. It is an evening star.

Now reverse your position; look toward the east, toward the sunrise. Have your friend hold a lighted flashlight in one hand below the table top — the horizon. He holds a ball in the other hand and above the table top. The ball (Venus) is visible before sunrise. Both the ball and flashlight are moved upward. The sun rises. Now the sky would be bright and Venus would not be visible in the day sky.

Because the orbit of Venus is between earth and sun, Venus appears to go through phases. Sometimes it is a small crescent, sometimes it is full, and sometimes new. You can prove this for yourself in the following manner.

Draw a large circle on a table top to represent the orbit of Venus. Place a flashlight at the center to represent the sun. In a darkened room, bend over until your eye is level with the table top. Put a ball at position 1 and shine the flashlight on it. What do you see? You will see a small crescent. This is what the astronomer sees through a telescope when he sees Venus in this position.

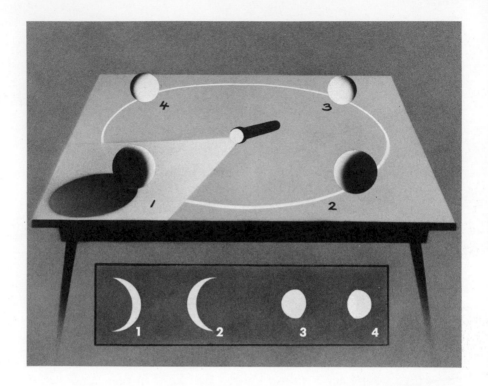

    Move Venus (the ball) to positions 2, 3, and 4, shining the light on it at each place. Notice the changed shape. Midway from 1 to 2 Venus is in front of the sun. The planet is much smaller in reality than the sun; and so, if it is in a direct line with the sun's disk, it would appear as a tiny speck against the sun. When this happens, we say that Venus transits the sun. Most of the time Venus is above or below the sun and so a transit does not occur. But it cannot be seen because of the glare of the sun. When it is midway from 3 to 4 it is behind the sun. Because the sun is much larger than Venus, the planet cannot be seen at all when this happens.

    When you observe Mars, Jupiter, and Saturn, you will notice that they rise in the east and set in the west, as the sun and moon do also. This motion from east to west is apparent, it is caused by the rotation of the earth.

You can show this quite easily. Stand with arms outstretched at your sides; your left hand is your eastern horizon, your right one the western horizon. Look toward your left at a distant object. Make a quarter turn toward the left, and now the object (a tree, for example) will be directly in front of you. Continue turning, and the tree will be seen off your right hand. The tree appeared to change position with respect to your left and right hands. Yet the tree did not move at all actually.

And so it is with the sun, stars, and planets; the rising and setting of them is produced by earth's rotation.

However, the planets do move actually; they change position against the background stars. All the planets move around the sun in the same direction. If an observer could get way out in space, above the North Pole far from the earth, and look back on the solar system, he would see the planets moving in a direction counter to the movements of clock hands. Astronomers say the planets move from west to east about the sun.

As we observe planets in our own sky, they move from west to east also. However, this motion appears to vary, for occasionally the planets appear to stop, to reverse direction for a few weeks, and then resume the west-to-east motion. We know that a planet cannot stop and reverse itself actually. Therefore, this motion must be apparent and not real. We call it retrograde, or backward, motion. A planet appears to move backward because our platform (the earth) does not revolve around the sun at the same speed as the planet under observation. For example, earth moves 18.5 miles per second in its path around the sun, Mars moves 15 miles per second. Earth completes a revolution in 365 days, Mars requires 687 days.

The next diagram shows why we see Mars move from west to east, appear to reverse itself, and then resume its west-to-east motion.

The inner circle shows the location of earth on seven successive

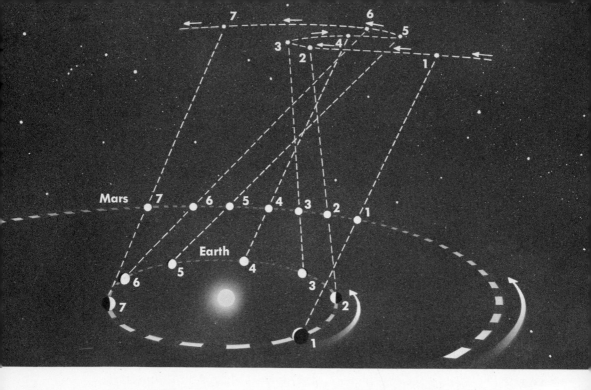

months. The outer circle shows the position of Mars during the same months. When we observe Mars from positions 1, 2, and 3, the planet is seen moving from west to east against the background stars. When seen from positions 4 and 5, Mars appears to be moving from east to west; it is retrograding. Then when seen from positions 5, 6, and 7, the planet has resumed its west-to-east motion.

These variations in the movement of Mars were noted by astronomers who lived several thousand years ago. They attempted to explain them, but could do so only by imagining that planets moved in great circles about another circle which went around the earth. The system was very complicated, and completely wrong. The supposition was not corrected until 1543 when Nicolaus Copernicus, a Polish astronomer, published the explanation given above.

You can see for yourself the changing position of Mars by plotting the planet on a star chart. From the table find when Mars will be in the evening sky. Note which constellation it is in, or the star that it is nearest. Make star maps similar to those in this book and then mark out on them the path of Mars as you see it move from constellation to constellation. Keep your chart for several weeks to note the changing position.

Keep a record of your observations of the planets, noting as accurately as possible their position and the way they appear. You might add the information you gather to this tabulation of facts about the planets.

Planet	Distance from Sun (miles)	Diameter (miles)	Speed Around Sun (miles per second)	Volume (number of earths it could contain)	Temperature (degrees Fahrenheit)
Mercury	36,000,000	3,010	29.8	0.05	700 sunlit side −400 dark side
Venus	67,200,000	7,610	21.8	0.89	130 sunlit side -13 at night
Earth	92,900,000	7,918	18.5	1.00	57 if measured from moon, -67 stratosphere
Mars	141,500,000	4,140	15.0	0.14	68 hottest side
Jupiter	483,300,000	86,900	8.1	1321.95	-200
Saturn	886,000,000	71,500	6.0	736.34	-238
Uranus	1,783,000,000	29,500	4.2	51.72	-275 } atmosphere
Neptune	2,791,000,000	26,800	3.4	38.78	-360
Pluto	3,671,000,000	3,600 (?)	2.9	0.09 (?)	-380

AURORAS

5

PEOPLE WHO live about 40° north of the equator can see the northern lights ten or twelve times in any one year. If you live farther south, you will not see the displays as often. However, northern lights have been seen as far south as Havana, Cuba. A spectacular display that occurred in February, 1958, was seen quite clearly by the observatory there. If you live farther north than 40°, you can see the northern lights frequently throughout the year, especially in the late fall and early spring.

The northern lights appear in an endless variety of forms and colors. Sometimes there is nothing more than a soft glow in the northern sky. Frequently one sees a great arch of soft light. The light pulsates slowly, and from time to time great needlelike streamers that look like searchlight beams emerge from it. They extend toward the zenith, the point in the sky that is directly overhead. The streamers build up in brightness, fade, and then subside completely.

Sometimes the display appears as a vast drapery in the sky. It looks like curtains, folded and pleated, slowly swinging in a breeze, changing constantly in shape and color. On certain occasions the display fills the entire sky. Great streamers radiate from the magnetic North Pole, spiraling outward to form a striking crown of light.

The northern lights are more properly called the aurora borealis.

58

The word *aurora* is Latin and it means "the dawn." *Borealis* is also Latin; it means "north." *Aurora borealis* means "dawn in the north." Aurora australis, the similar display that occurs in the south polar region, means "dawn in the south."

Scientists have studied auroras for some time and they have obtained considerable information about them. For example, auroras are probably visible at times over the entire night side of the earth. Continuous arcs have been seen for over 2,000 miles, and displays occurring at the same time have been observed from England to Ohio. Auroras occur in the Arctic and Antarctic at the same time. However, there are many questions that remain to be answered. We shall consider here explanations concerning the northern lights that are believed to be true. For example, we know that auroras may have no color at all. But more often they will be a soft apple green. Rose, lavender, yellow, and violet are often observed. Curtain auroras are usually yellow-green tipped with rose-red along the lower edge.

Displays can be seen almost every evening from Alaska, Canada, and Greenland. However, when there are flares on the surface of the sun, the displays are much more intense. Solar flares, which appear to be associated with sunspots, are observed from earth as areas of greatly increased temperature and brightness of a small part of the solar surface. The region flares up very brightly and then quiets down. When intense solar flares are reported, we can anticipate strong auroras some 20 to 30 hours later.

It is believed that, when a solar flare occurs, great masses of electrons are ejected from the sun. These electrons travel through space covering several hundreds of miles each second. Some of the electrons approach the earth. However, in order to come close to the surface, the electrons must penetrate the magnetic field that surrounds our planet. We do not know the pattern of earth's magnetic field; but, based upon preliminary reports from rockets and satel-

lites and upon other studies, we believe that the magnetic field might be represented as shown by the light bands in the diagram. Notice that the angle of the field to the surface of the earth varies. Along the equatorial region, the magnetic field is concentric to the surface. In the polar regions, the magnetic field tapers in until it reaches the surface.

Electrons from the sun cannot penetrate the magnetic field easily. Only those possessing a large amount of energy get through. Electrons are more likely to follow along the magnetic field than to go through it. Indeed, electrons do follow earth's magnetic field, and so they tend to concentrate at the magnetic poles.

But the electrons do not reach the earth. They collide with particles in the ionosphere, a layer of the atmosphere that begins about 60 miles above the surface. The ionosphere is a layer of the atmosphere that contains ions, atoms that have an unusual number of electrons. Ordinarily, an atom has the same number of protons (positive charges) as it has electrons (negative charges). The positive charges equal the negative charges, and so the atom is electrically neutral. When an atom has more electrons than usual, the atom becomes a negative ion. When the atom has fewer electrons than normal, the atom is a positive ion. The ions in the ionosphere are positive; they attract electrons, particles that carry negative charges.

The electrons of an atom are arranged in shells, one shell inside another. When electrons shift from one shell to another, the atom (or ion) gives off energy. The energy may be in the form of X rays, heat, light. Electrons from the sun strike ions in the ionosphere. Some of them knock electrons from the ions, causing a shift in the remaining electrons from one shell to another. As the shift occurs, energy is released. The energy may be in the form of visible light. Different ions produce different colors; for example, certain oxygen ions produce green, certain nitrogen ions produce red.

Ordinary fluorescent lights operate in a manner similar to the northern lights. The glass cylinder contains mercury vapor, and the inside of the cylinder is coated with fluorescent paint. When electricity goes through mercury vapor, the vapor produces ultraviolet light. This light is invisible. The ultraviolet light falls upon the fluorescent paint. Atoms of the paint take in some of the energy of the ultraviolet light. The electrons in the atoms change position. As they do, energy is released from the atoms in the form of visible light.

We do not know how far into space ions extend. One way of measuring the extent of the ions is to find how high the aurora displays occur. A Norwegian scientist, Carl Störmer, has found auroras as high as 680 miles above the earth. He worked with Birkeland, who was stationed 20 miles away. The two men observed an aurora at the same time. To one observer, the band of light appeared to the right of the planet Venus. To the other observer, Venus appeared at the center of the same band. By measuring the apparent shift, the men could compute the height of the aurora. Perhaps satellites and space stations will enable us to define clearly the extent of the band around the earth that contains ions. At present it is believed to extend from 60 to 680 miles — the lowest and highest elevations at which the phenomenon of auroras has been observed.

The beauty of the aurora displays is awesome. Seeing them for the first time from northern latitudes is a breathtaking experience, one that is not soon forgotten. To observe auroras we suggest that you become familiar with the nighttime sky in your neighborhood. Know the direction of cities. Know which way is north. If there are no cities north of you, or other causes of a glow in the northern sky, a soft glow or gentle arc will be an aurora. Keep on the lookout, for your first sighting of an aurora is ample payment for all your efforts.

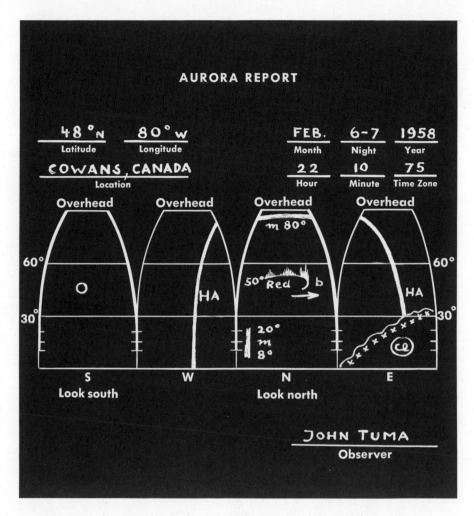

The sighting of auroras is exciting; however, the recording of observations should be part of your work, for conclusions about the nature of these auroras can be made only when considerable data are available.

During the IGY (International Geophysical Year), reports of auroras were sent to Cornell University. The report card that observers used is reproduced here. Make copies of it, and keep a file of your own aurora sightings. If you do this work carefully, the

HA (Homogeneous arc)

RA (Rayed arc)

R (Rays)   **PA (Pulsating arc)**   **PS (Pulsating spot)**

F (Flames)   **G (Glow)**   **S (Spot or patch)**

Auroral Data Center at Cornell University, Ithaca, New York, would welcome the information that you gather.

INTERPRETATION OF AURORA REPORT

The report was for 10:10 P.M. E.S.T., February 6, 1958. Time in the report is 22:10 (the 24-hour clock is used). In this method of time-keeping, all numbers beyond 12 (except 24) are P.M.; for example, 13:00 is 1:00 P.M., 16:00 is 4:00 P.M., and so on.

Beginning at the left, we read the report as follows.

No aurora (*o*) was seen in the south.

A homogeneous arc (*HA*) — homogeneous means the same throughout — extended from the western horizon to an altitude of 80° in the north, and it extended toward the east where it was obscured by a bank of clouds 30° above the horizon. The arc was of medium intensity, as indicated by the small *m* in front of 80°. No color is indicated; therefore the aurora was either colorless or yellow-green.

Toward north there was a bright (*b*) rayed arc at an altitude of 50°. The arc drifted toward the east. The lower part of it was red.

Rays of medium (*m*) intensity appeared in the northwest. They were vertical and extended from 8° to 20° above the horizon.

The various forms of auroras are shown on the facing page. Additional code letters are: *S* for spotty, *P* for pulsating, *G* for glow, *F* for flame, *W* for weak.

THE STARS

6

SELECT A clear cloudless night for viewing the stars. Also, if possible, select a location removed from a city so that the view is not obscured by the glow of advertising signs and city lights. Allow time for your eyes to adjust to the darkness, and remember your directions.

During any complete rotation of the earth, the same stars pass overhead. But we see only those stars that are overhead during the night hours. Because the earth goes around the sun, we see different stars at different seasons. The principal stars and constellations visible in the northern sky at various seasons of the year are shown in the charts here, which apply to the four seasons. Each chart is based on a constellation that is easy to locate — and the other stars can be found by using that constellation as a starting point.

In our discussion of stars, the term magnitude is used. A star's magnitude is expressed as a number. It tells us how the brightness of the star compares with the brightness of other stars. Ptolemy, an Egyptian, classified stars about two thousand years ago into six divisions, or magnitudes. The brightest stars had the smallest magnitude. The twenty brightest stars were described as 1st magnitude. As the stars became dimmer, they were called 2nd, 3rd magnitude, and so on. The dimmest stars visible to the naked eye were described as 6th magnitude.

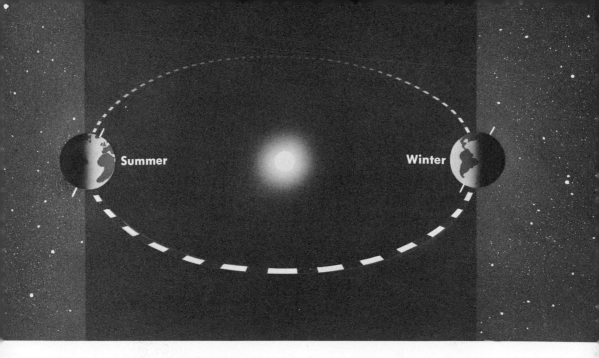

Summer

Winter

As telescopes were developed, men found that Ptolemy's divisions were very crude indeed. Also, telescopes were able to "see" multitudes of stars far beyond human vision. Therefore, even though the old system of magnitudes is still used today, it has been modified. Sir John Herschel in the nineteenth century established that one magnitude is 2.5 times brighter than the following magnitude. For example, a 2nd-magnitude star is 2.5 times brighter than a 3rd-magnitude star; a 1st-magnitude star is 2.5 times brighter than a 2nd; a 0-magnitude star 2.5 times brighter than a 1st magnitude; and a —1 magnitude is 2.5 times brighter than one of 0 magnitude.

Keep in mind that the smaller the number, the greater the magnitude. The sun is the brightest object in the sky; its magnitude is —26.8. The magnitude of the full moon is —12.6. Accurate measurements of the brightness of stars enable a closer separation of magnitudes, and so magnitude is often expressed in decimal fractions of whole numbers. Magnitudes of some stars are given in the table here. We suggest that you learn a few of them so you will be able to make comparisons with other stars and thus in a crude manner estimate the magnitudes of such stars.

Star	Magnitude	Star	Magnitude
Sirius	−1.43	Spica	1.00
Vega	0.04	Deneb	1.26
Arcturus	0.06	Regulus	1.34
Rigel	0.15	Bellatrix	1.70
Betelgeuse	0.70	Polaris	2.12
Altair	0.89	Denebola	2.23
Antares	0.98		

Most people cannot see objects beyond the 6th magnitude. This is the limit, you might say, of visibility with the unaided eye. Telescopes can register objects so dim that they would be classified in the 20th magnitude. A first magnitude object is 100,000,000 times brighter than an object of the 20th magnitude.

One of the big difficulties in identifying stars is the constant change in the position of star patterns due to the rotation of the earth and due to changes in the location of the observer. However, the pattern of the stars does not change in our lifetime, for the stars are essentially fixed in the sky. The only change is the angle from which we view them.

Take the charts outside and use a flashlight to view them. Cover the flashlight with red cellophane or paint the bulb with red nail polish. When you are looking at the sky during the winter, for example, if the winter stars (Orion group) are on the meridian, the stars of fall (Pegasus group) are toward the west and the stars of spring (Leo, which is a part of the Dipper group) are toward the east. If the chart is placed on its left side, it shows the arrangement of the stars when the constellation (for which the chart is named) is rising; when the chart is placed on its right side, the arrangement is the same as that which can be seen when that constellation is setting.

The groups of stars are overlapped at the border to aid in placing

THE DIPPER GROUP

Dubhe

BIG DIPPER

Merak

Alphecca

Arcturus

LEO

Regulus

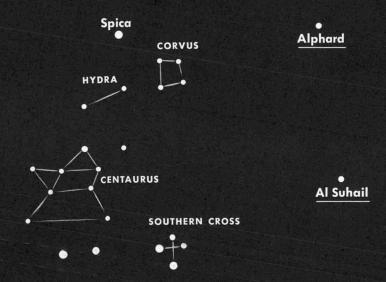

Spica

CORVUS

Alphard

HYDRA

CENTAURUS

Al Suhail

SOUTHERN CROSS

the group in relation to the other groups. Names of those stars that serve as connectors between groups are underlined on the charts.

THE DIPPER GROUP (SPRINGTIME STARS)

At this time, Merak and Dubhe, the two pointers of the Big Dipper, are in a generally north-south position. If you continue northward from them, you reach Polaris. If you follow a line southward from them, you arrive at Leo and the bright star Regulus. A continuation carries you to Alphard.

Regulus is often identified as being the end of the handle of the sickle, or some think of it as the period of a reversed question mark. East of the sickle is a triangle with the bright star Denebola.

Alioth, Mizar, and Alkaid, three stars in the handle of the Dipper, form an arc. If you follow this arc along, you find Arcturus in the curve of the arc. It is 1st magnitude and therefore very bright. Continue along the curve of the arc and you arrive at Spica, another bright star. Just beyond Spica, and slightly west of it is Corvus, frequently called the Cutter's Mainsail, or Spica's Spanker.

Alphecca in the crown just east of Arcturus connects the Leo group with Scorpio in the east. Alphard and a line from Arcturus through Regulus connects with the Orion group in the west.

THE SUMMER TRIANGLE GROUP (THE STARS OF SUMMER)

The summer triangle contains three 1st-magnitude stars, Altair, Deneb, and Vega. Actually, there is no constellation called the summer triangle; each of these stars is in a different constellation.

Altair may be identified by two small stars, one on either side of it. These are often called the guardians. However, the guardian star to the south is only a 4th-magnitude star, and therefore it is not usually visible on hazy nights or when there is bright moonlight. When the three stars are visible, the identification of Altair is positive, for the arrangement is unique.

THE SUMMER TRIANGLE GROUP

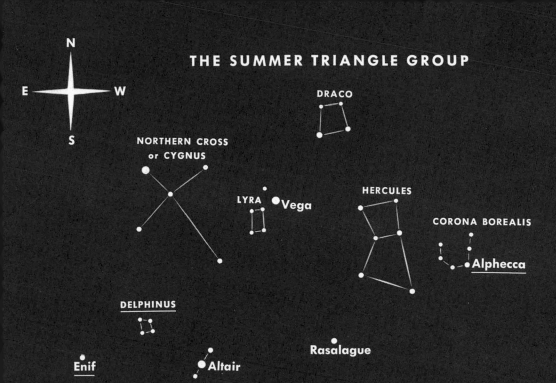

N
E **W**
S

DRACO

NORTHERN CROSS
or CYGNUS

LYRA ●**Vega**

HERCULES

CORONA BOREALIS

●**Alphecca**

DELPHINUS

Rasalague

Enif

●**Altair**

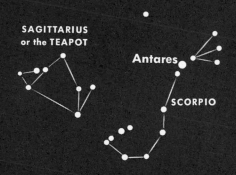

SAGITTARIUS
or the TEAPOT

Antares

SCORPIO

Peacock

TRIANGULUM AUSTRAL

Deneb is the first star in the upright of the Northern Cross. It is sometimes considered to be the tail of Cygnus, the Swan, another name for this constellation. The eastern arm of the cross points toward Enif and the western arm toward Etamin. The bisectors of the lower right angles of the cross point toward Altair and toward Vega.

Vega is a bright star that is easy to see. When haze is absent and when the sky is dark, one can see an almost perfect parallelogram slightly south and east of the star. Because all stars in the figure are dim, one cannot see them clearly at all times, and so they cannot be relied upon to locate Vega.

By continuing southward with the upright of the Northern Cross about three times the distance between Deneb and Albireo, the star at the base, you come to Antares, the bright star in the constellation Scorpio. This is one constellation that appears like the animal after which it is named. The curve from Antares to Shaula, the tip of the tail, is especially suggestive of the tail section of a scorpion. Directly east of Scorpio is Sagittarius. We represent it as a teapot rather than an archer, as it is usually shown, because it is easier to recognize this way.

Hercules is another constellation in this group, although it is not outstanding, for none of the stars in it are bright. However, this constellation contains the most direct pointers for Rasalague, a star used by navigators. As can be seen, this star is also in a line connecting Vega and Antares. Just west of Hercules is Corona Borealis, the Northern Crown. The bright star Alphecca is outstanding in this group.

THE PEGASUS GROUP (THE FALL STARS)

The square of Pegasus dominates the sky at this time, and sky watchers can use it as a point of departure. Actually, the square is not a single constellation, for Alpheratz is in the constellation

THE PEGASUS GROUP

N
E · W
S

CASSIOPEIA

ella

PLEIADES

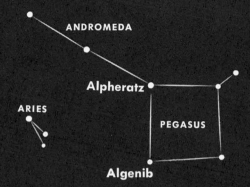

ANDROMEDA

Alpheratz

ARIES

PEGASUS

Algenib

DELPHINUS

Enif

Fomalhaut

GRUS

Peacock

Andromeda. We might think of Andromeda as consisting of Alpheratz, Mirach, and Almach. If we follow in a gentle arc from one star to the other, we arrive at Marfak and Capella. Andromeda leads us into Alpheratz, and enables identification of Markab, which is in the opposite corner.

A line from Scheat through Markab points almost directly to Fomalhaut, a bright star in Piscis Australis, the Southern Fish.

A line from Alpheratz through Algenib leads one to Diphda and Achernar. Acamar forms a triangle with the latter two.

A line from Algenib through Alpheratz points to Caph in Cassiopeia. Continue along the same line to Polaris.

Hamal in the constellation Aries lies directly east of the square of Pegasus. The First Point of Aries lies slightly west of the midpoint of a line joining Algenib and Diphda. Spring occurs when the sun is at this point in the sky.

Capella connects this group with the Orion group in the east; and Enif serves to link the group to the west. A line from Scheat through Eta Pegasus leads to Deneb, and so we have another connection with the western group.

THE ORION GROUP (THE WINTER STARS)

Orion is the most impressive of all the constellations. Next to the Big Dipper, it is the most well-known throughout the world. Betelgeuse, a beautiful reddish star; and Rigel, a brilliant bright blue star, together with the three stars of the belt, make the constellation most impressive.

Continue the line of the belt to the south and east and you arrive at Sirius. This is the brightest star in the sky. It has a magnitude of —1.43. It is often called the nose of Orion's hunting dog—Canis Major. By continuing the line of the belt in the opposite direction, you arrive at the Pleiades. At the present time 6 stars in this group are visible to the untrained eye. Some skilled observers say they can

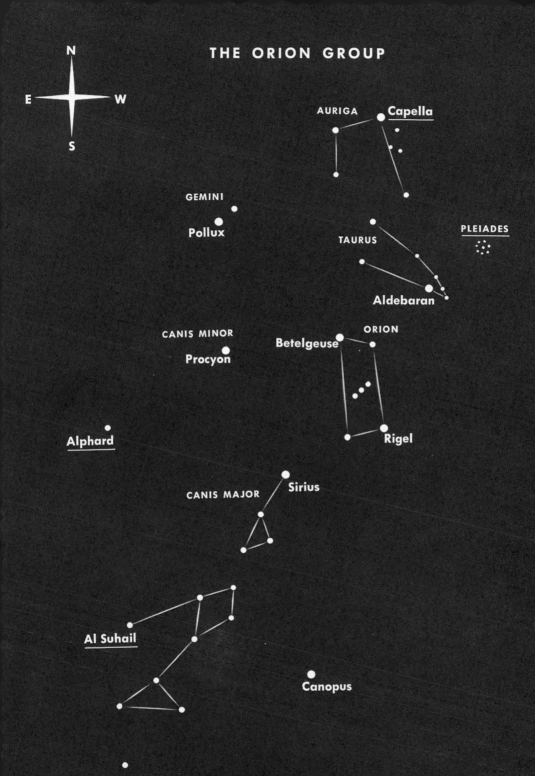

THE ORION GROUP

N
E W
S

AURIGA **Capella**

GEMINI

Pollux

PLEIADES

TAURUS

Aldebaran

CANIS MINOR

Procyon

Betelgeuse ORION

Alphard

Rigel

Sirius

CANIS MAJOR

Al Suhail

Canopus

see 8 and sometimes 9 here. Telescopically there are scores of stars in this segment. See how many you can detect. About halfway between Orion and the Pleiades, and slightly north of a line connecting them, is Aldebaran in the constellation Taurus. This star can be identified because it is one of a group that forms a *V* in the sky.

A line from Aldebaran through Rigel carries one to Canopus. This star is in a southerly direction from Orion.

A line from Rigel through Alnilam carries one to Castor. Next to this star is Pollux, the two comprising the principal stars in Gemini, the Twins.

Capella, the northernmost of the bright stars is located by continuing a soft arc from Rigel through Aldebaran, and on to Capella. It is the bright star in Auriga, a constellation that is five-sided and looks somewhat like a misshapen home plate.

Another way to locate the various bright stars we have been discussing is to think of a circle passing through the following stars: Sirius, Rigel, Aldebaran, Capella, Pollux, Procyon.

The Pleiades link this group with the stars to the west, and Alphard and Al Suhail connect the group with the stars in the eastern group.

THE POLAR GROUP (ALL SEASONS)

There are four principal constellations in the region of the North Pole of the sky; they are Cassiopeia, the Big Dipper, the Little Dipper, and Draco.

Merak and Dubhe, the pointer stars, locate Polaris, as discussed under the Dipper Group. If one continues along this line, he comes to Caph in Cassiopeia.

When Cassiopeia is above the Pole Star, the Big Dipper is below, and vice versa.

The two Dippers appear to be pouring one into the other. The

THE POLAR GROUP

CASSIOPEIA

Caph

DRACO

LITTLE DIPPER

Polaris

BIG DIPPER

Dubhe

Merak

Little Dipper helps to locate Polaris and Kochab. It is interesting to note that Polaris is not directly at the North Pole; it is removed by about 1°.

Draco is about halfway from Cassiopeia to the Big Dipper. Etamin, the bright star in Draco, is more easily found by following the western arm of the Northern Cross as was shown in that group. Marfak is best identified by following the directions given under the Pegasus Group.

STAR TRAILS AND THE SKY CLOCK

If you have a camera with a time exposure adjustment, you can make a photograph of the northern sky. It is exciting and challenging, and the picture provides a fine illustration of the apparent daily motion of the stars.

Select a location that is free of street lights, automobile lights, and all other kinds of lighting; a place that has little ambient (surrounding) light. Also, select a night when there is no moon, and the stars are clear and bright. Load your camera with fast panchromatic film. Mount it on a firm support, and aim it at Polaris, centering that star as nearly as possible on the finder.

Open the stop to its widest aperture, open the shutter and leave it open for an hour. The picture you obtain will look somewhat like the illustration on the facing page. Each bright star leaves a record on the negative.

Such photographs of the northern sky show that some of the constellations never set; that is, they appear to move around a circle in the sky, remaining above the horizon continuously. Other stars, parts of constellations, dip below the horizon briefly, rising again after only a few hours. The farther the stars are removed from the center of the circle, Polaris, the longer they remain below the horizon, and the farther south will be their points of rising and setting.

It is interesting to note that there is no star located precisely at the North Pole of the sky. Polaris happens to be the star which, at the present time, is closest to the pole; however, as we have said, it is removed from the pole by about 1°. Thuban, in Draco, was the Pole Star some 5,000 years ago.

As you look toward the polar constellations, facing north, the stars appear to move in a counterclockwise direction; they appear to move opposite to the direction of the hands of a clock. They rise in the east and set in the west.

The counterclockwise motion of the polar stars, and the movement of all the stars from east to west, is caused by the rotation of the earth. The stars do not really move in this fashion, and so *apparent motion* is a more accurate way of referring to the motions. The stars *appear* to move from east to west only because earth, the platform from which we are viewing the stars, moves from west to east.

Make photographs of stars in other parts of the sky. You will find that the streaks of light on your print are straight lines. The angle that the light streaks make with the eastern horizon line becomes larger as you move toward the equator. The streaks are 90° to the horizon at the equator; they go straight up.

If you measure the arcs made by the stars on your one-hour polar photograph, you will find that each of the arcs is about 1/24 of a circle. That is, it requires 24 hours for each star to complete the circle and return to its original position. Actually, the time required is 4 minutes less than 24 hours, so the polar stars can be considered as a clock that gains 4 minutes on our clock in 24 hours. Let us see how this clock of the stars can be put to use.

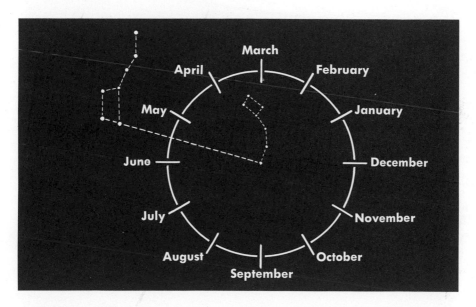

Imagine that the northern sky is a huge clock face with Polaris at the center. The face is divided into twelve equal sections. Instead of being numbered from 1 through 12, they are labeled after the months of the year. The order of labeling is counterclockwise. March is at the top of the dial, April at the 11 position, May at the 10, and so on. The twelve months of the year are represented. This clock of the sky is a 24-hour clock, and so each division is equivalent to a two-hour interval.

Merak and Dubhe, the pointer stars of the Big Dipper, indicate the time in the following manner. Suppose we find May 15 on the clock dial. If you look into the north sky at midnight on that date, you will find that the pointers are in line directly above the location of that date. At midnight on any particular date the pointers are directly in line with that date on the clock face.

If the date happens to be March 15 and the pointers are above the May 15 position, the time is 4 hours after midnight; four o'clock in the morning. On the other hand, if the date is June 15, and if the pointers are above the May 15 position, the time is 2 hours before midnight; ten o'clock in the evening. With a little practice, the sky watcher will find that the sky clock is a reliable timepiece.

The sky clock illustrates an interesting situation: the fact that all the stars pass overhead during every 24-hour period. However, even though stars are overhead both day and night, we can see stars only at night when the sky is dark and there is contrast.

The positions that the stars occupy at any time of the day and at any time of the year can be predicted by using a chart that translates star time to clock time in the manner explained below. The polar stars appear to move around Polaris. Also, we know that the pointer stars of the Dipper are directly above a location on the dial of the sky clock at midnight on the indicated date. Consider the sky clock as a circular dial with an arrow beginning at Polaris and point-

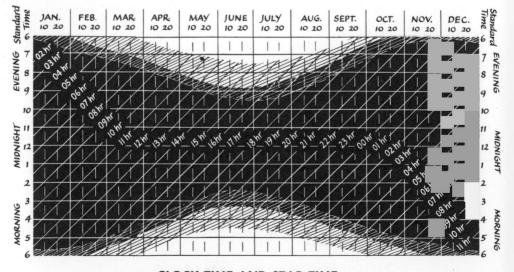

CLOCK TIME AND STAR TIME

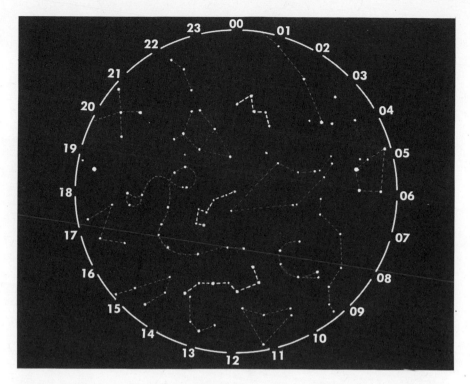

ing straight upward. The edge of the dial is divided into 24 equal sections, and these are numbered from 0 to 24. The chart of polar stars, as we have drawn it, stands at 0 hours star time. Refer to the chart of star times and clock times. Find the line for 0 hours *star time*. Follow it, and you find that 0 hours star time occurs at 4:00 A.M. clock time on July 25, at 2:00 A.M. on August 25, at 12:00 A.M. clock time on July 30, at 2:00 A.M. on August 25, at 12:00 midnight on September 25, and so on. On these dates at the times indicated, the stars will be in the positions shown.

You can determine the positions that the stars will occupy at any time as follows. Select any date. Suppose it is March 10, and suppose that the time you are interested in is 10:00 P.M. On March 10 at 10:00 P.M., the star time will be about 9 hours, the diagonal line. Turn the star chart until 9 is upright to see the positions that the stars will occupy at the time.

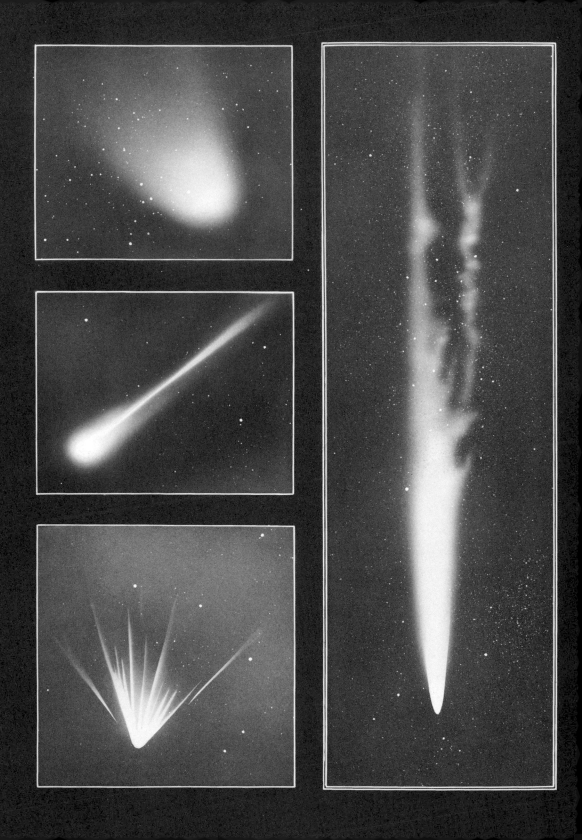

COMETS

7

PHOTOGRAPHS OF comets often show a great, bright central region and a long wispy tail. People mistake the tail for a bright trail such as those produced by meteors. Therefore, people who have never observed the slow motion of a comet mistakenly believe that comets streak across the sky, appearing and disappearing in a matter of minutes. Even though comets move very fast through outer space, they are so far away from us that they move very slowly across our sky. As a matter of fact, they may be visible for several days from any particular location on earth; sometimes they can be seen for two weeks or more.

Using telescopes, astronomers see two new comets, on the average, every year, and they also see some four or more comets that have been observed previously. More than a thousand comets have been observed and recorded. Astronomers believe there must be hundreds of thousands in our solar system. Some few people believe there may be millions of them. Comets move in large orbits; some of the orbits, as in the case of Halley's comet, extend out beyond the orbit of Neptune. They become visible only when they are relatively close to the earth, moving toward the sun or away from it.

The majority of comets are dim and distant, and so they cannot be seen with the unaided eye. However, comets are bright occasionally, and sky watchers are able to see them very well indeed without using binoculars or telescopes. In both the spring and fall of 1957 new comets appeared which were extremely visible. The first comet was called Arend-Roland, after two Belgian astronomers who discovered it. The one in the fall was called Comet Mrkos after a Czechoslovakian astronomer who first identified it. Both of these comets were visible for several evenings, changing position against the background stars as they moved around the sun and then off into space.

Halley's comet, one of the most well known, was named after the English astronomer who plotted its orbit and predicted its return. It was last seen in 1910. It has a period of seventy-five years, and so should be visible again in 1985. This comet was known in the third century before Christ. It is very bright, so bright that many people who saw it in 1910 believed that it was going to collide with the earth. Actually, earth did go through the tail of Halley's Comet at that time; however, we noticed nothing unusual. This is because the material in the tail is spread out thinly. It has been suggested that the amount of material within a thousand cubic miles of a comet's tail is less than that in a cubic inch of ordinary air at sea level.

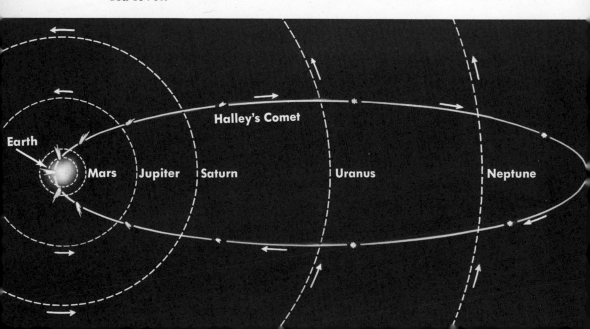

A bright comet appears as a fuzzy region of the sky, and usually a tail is associated with it. When a comet is far from the sun, various kinds of ices probably make up most of the object. There may be bits of solid materials embedded in the frozen matter. As the comet nears the sun, changes occur. Brightness increases, a tail develops, sometimes the comet seems to break into two parts.

The head of a comet is made up of a bright region, or coma. Toward the center of the coma brightness increases, and very often a nucleus or core of intense brightness appears.

Not all comets develop tails. When they do have them, the tails may be several million miles long. The tail of Halley's comet was 100 million miles long. The record length was the tail of the Great Comet of 1843. This tail was 300 million miles long, more than three times the distance between the earth and the sun.

As comets near the sun, some of the frozen materials change to gases because of intense heating. The gases are very nebulous, and so pressure exerted by sunlight pushes them away from the head of the comet. As the comet nears the sun, the gases trail behind the head, producing a long, misty veil. As the comet moves away from the sun, the gases are still pushed away from the head. The tail precedes the head, much as though it were a flashlight beam, lighting the path of the comet. As the comet moves farther from the sun, the tail diminishes in size, and finally it disappears completely.

Look for a small, cloudlike region in the sky, one that appears motionless, but which changes position slightly from night to night. If you are quite sure you are looking at a comet, call your local newspaper or the nearest observatory or planetarium.

Watch your local newspaper for news about new comets. No one can tell when a comet will be discovered, or how bright it will be; however, your chances of seeing several naked-eye comets during your lifetime are very good indeed.

Meteor showers, discussed in chapter 8, are related to comets. As a comet goes through space, it loses some of the material of which it is made. Particles of matter, such as grains of sand, and considerably smaller particles separate from the head of the comet. They spread out in a band, or ribbon. Astronomers refer to such ribbons or clusters of small particles as a comet gravel bank. When earth moves into the region, many of the particles pass through our atmosphere, producing a meteor shower.

No one knows for sure where comets come from. Their origin is no better known than the origin of the solar system itself. They have been referred to as "sweepers of the sky," perhaps because some people believe they form as gas particles gather together to form the nucleus. Some astronomers believe that the region of the solar system abounds with billions of comets, and that occasionally the gravitational attraction of the sun pulls one into an orbit, causing it to circulate through the system of planets.

Comets contain a number of materials. The elements carbon, hydrogen, oxygen, and nitrogen have been identified. And molecules of cyanogen (CN), methane (CH), carbon monoxide (CO), nitrogen (N_2), carbon (C_2), nitrogen hydride (NH), and hydroxyl (OH) have been identified.

Comets do not produce their own light. The light of a comet is produced by reflected sunlight and by sunlight which is absorbed and then re-emitted. Solid particles in the comet reflect light. Molecules of gas absorb and re-emit the light. The gaseous molecules take in large amounts of ultraviolet light from the sun. The invisible ultraviolet activates the molecules, causing them to give off various colors of visible light. The action is similar to that which occurs in fluorescent lights, where ultraviolet (invisible) light falls upon a phosphor which produces visible light. Therefore, comets may appear slightly bluish or reddish when certain gases dominate just as fluorescent tubes do, although they are more often white because all wave lengths are combined.

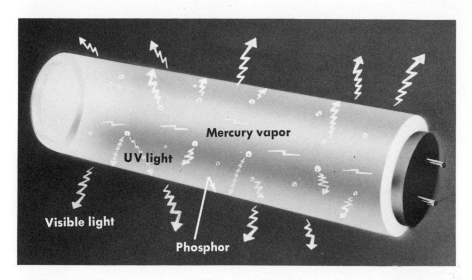

Sir Isaac Newton, an English mathematician, proved that comets move in paths that are either elliptical or parabolic. An ellipse or a parabola can be produced by sectioning a cone, as directed below.

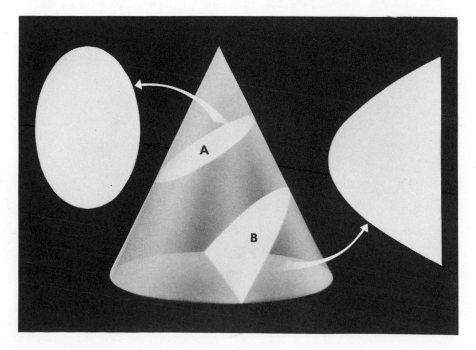

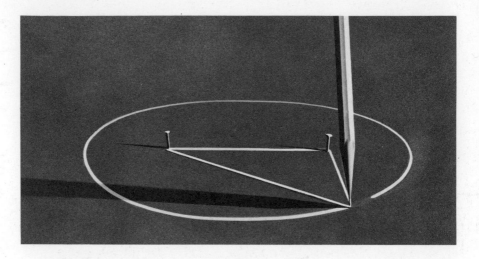

Fashion a cone from clay, and then slice it in the manner indicated in the diagram. The surface exposed at *A* will be an ellipse, and the surface exposed at *B* will be a parabola. A parabola never closes. That is, an object moving in a path shaped this way would travel into space, never returning. Comets tend to move in flat ellipses, almost parabolas. They may be deflected by a planet into a rounder orbit or into an open one that takes them out of the solar system.

You can make an ellipse in another way. Stick two pins upright in a piece of cardboard. Make a loop of string and place it over the pins. Insert a pencil in the loop, and draw a line, keeping the string tight at all times. The figure that results is an ellipse. The farther apart the pins are, the flatter the ellipse will be.

You can construct a parabola as follows. Draw a line $2\frac{1}{2}$ inches long and mark off each quarter inch. Construct uprights from each point. You obtain the length of the uprights by working this out: $10 \times 0 = 0$, $9 \times 1 = 9$, $8 \times 2 = 16$, $7 \times 3 = 21$, $6 \times 4 = 24$, $5 \times 5 = 25$, $4 \times 6 = 24$, and so on. The answers tell you how many quarter-inches long each line should be. Draw the lines and then connect them. The curve will be a parabola.

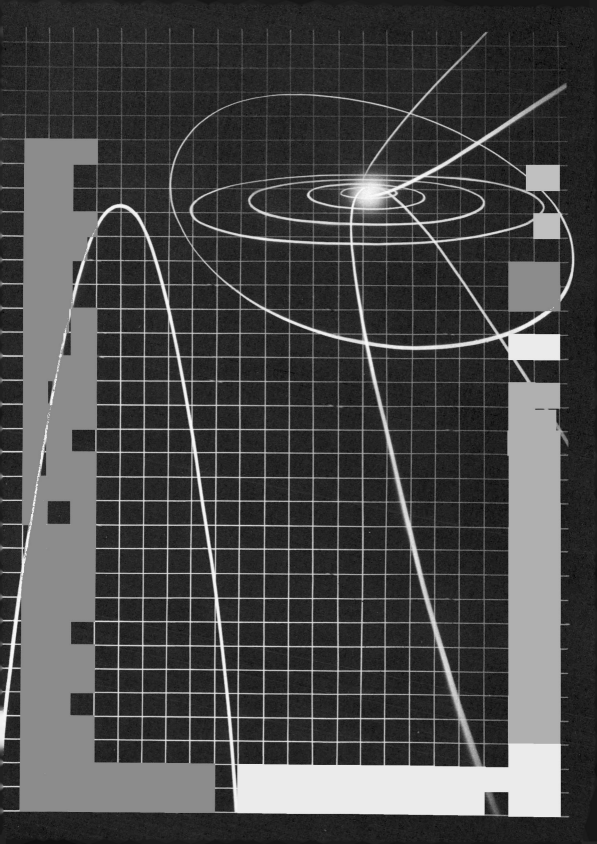

METEORS AND METEORITES

8

METEORS ARE streaks of light in the sky that are often called shooting stars. They are produced by small particles of matter (meteoroids) that become white hot as they pass through the atmosphere. The light streak trailing behind the meteoroid is white-hot particles given off by the meteoroid, submicroscopic in size, and molecules of gases glowing because of the high temperature. About twenty million of these meteoroids enter our atmosphere every day, producing light streaks that can be seen with the unaided eye. If we included those light streaks so dim that binoculars or telescopes are needed to see them, the total would be several times twenty million. The dust and debris of these meteoroids sift down through our atmosphere and land on the earth. Some people estimate that this dust adds 4,000 pounds of mass to the earth every twenty-four hours.

If the sky is black and free of the glow produced by city lights, advertising signs, and automobile headlights, you should see five or ten meteors during any one-hour interval. You cannot expect to step outside and see meteors immediately, for your eyes must first become dark adapted. Dark adaptation means the wide opening of the pupils of your eyes to admit more light; the retina of the eye becomes more sensitive, so a small amount of light excites it. The result is that you are better able to see dimly lighted objects. Dark adaptation is achieved rapidly in young people; it may take twenty minutes or so in older people.

Meteoroids abound in outer space. We see them only when they enter our atmosphere, become white hot, and so produce a streak of light. Sometimes the displays last the merest fraction of a second, and they are very dim. Occasionally, meteors appear very bright, brighter than the brightest stars. They are then called fireballs. Displays bright enough to light up the entire countryside have been reported, although they are rare occurrences. The interior temperature of a meteoroid in outer space must be very low. When a meteoroid enters earth's atmosphere, friction causes the exterior to become very hot. The interior is still extremely cold. Uneven expansion caused by the uneven temperature produces stresses and strains within the meteoroid. Sometimes these stresses are severe enough to cause the meteoroid to explode with a loud sound that can be heard over a wide region. Such an exploding meteoroid is called a bolide, after the Greek *bolis*, which means "missile." Bolides may occur in the sky over any part of the world; however, they are rare.

Meteors occur about 50 to 75 miles above the earth, well within our own atmosphere. The smaller disappear at a height of about 40 miles. They flash across the sky at speeds between 10 and 40 miles per second (mps); the average speed is 26 mps.

Although the average velocity of meteoroids is 26 mps, this would not be the impact velocity, should they collide with the earth. The earth moves about 18.5 miles per second in its path about the sun. Therefore, if a meteoroid were to collide with earth head on, the speed of impact would equal the speed of earth plus the speed of the meteoroid: 26 plus 18.5, or 44.5 mps. If a meteoroid caught up with the earth, the speed of impact would equal the speed of the meteoroid less the speed of the earth: 26 minus 18.5, or 7.5 mps.

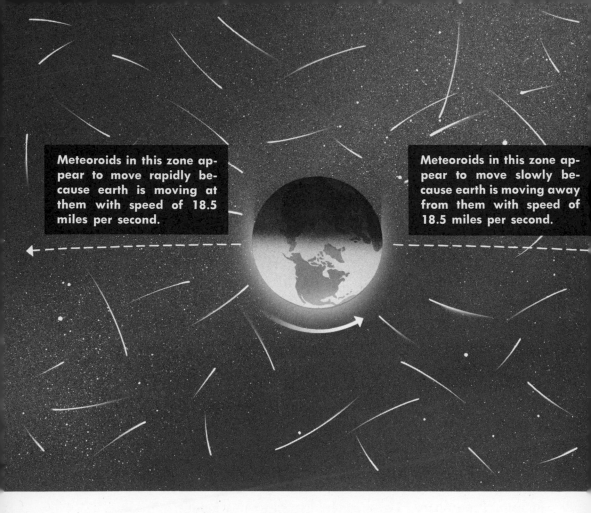

Meteoroids in this zone appear to move rapidly because earth is moving at them with speed of 18.5 miles per second.

Meteoroids in this zone appear to move slowly because earth is moving away from them with speed of 18.5 miles per second.

The best time for watching the sky for meteors is after midnight. About twice as many can be seen at that time as are visible before midnight because at that time you are on the front half of the earth as it moves around the sun. Therefore, we see those meteors which we overtake, as well as those which catch up with us. Before midnight, you are on the back half of the earth and you see only those meteors that catch up with the earth.

The American Meteor Society is interested in receiving reports of sightings. For report forms and directions for making reports, write to Dr. C. P. Olivier, American Meteor Society, 521 North Wynnewood Avenue, Narberth, Pennsylvania.

When you are sky watching, plot the positions of meteors and the paths they follow on a star chart. Construct a chart, similar to the one in chapter 6, that is appropriate for the time of year when you are making the observations. When you see a meteor, draw the path of it on your sky chart. Continue doing this for an hour or so.

You will sometimes find that the meteors in a display appear to come from one part of the sky. A region of the sky where meteors appear to originate is the radiant. Meteors seen near the radiant will have short paths. Those seen at the radiant will appear motionless. You observe a light that brightens and then fades out completely because the meteor is in your line of sight—it is moving directly toward you.

Even though they may appear to do so, meteors do not emerge from one single point in the sky actually. They appear to do so because of an optical illusion. The effect is similar to the manner in which railroad rails appear to approach each other as distance increases, even though we know they do not.

Meteors that appear to move from a radiant are part of a meteor stream. Astronomers call a stream by the name of the constellation in which the point of the radiant appears to be located: the Perseid stream refers to Perseus, the Leonids to Leo, the Andromedes to Andromeda.

Meteor streams follow elliptical orbits around the sun. The particles that compose the stream are debris ejected by a comet as it speeds through the space of the inner planetary system. Whenever the earth passes into, or near, a stream, a meteor shower is likely.

During meteor showers, thousands of light streaks may be visible. In modern times we have had no sensational displays; in fact, you would be fortunate to see thirty-or forty meteors in a sixty-minute interval. However, on November 12, 1833, there was a shower that must have been awesome, for some 35,000 meteors were observed per hour. The entire sky was full of meteors and fireballs. Many of them appeared as large as the full moon, and they left trails that lasted for fifteen to twenty minutes.

We suggest that you try to observe meteors any night when conditions for observing are good, when the sky is free of clouds, the moon is not out, the sky is black. And certainly, you should plan to do sky watching during meteor showers. The dates for the most impressive showers are given in the table.

Date		Name of Shower	Origin of Name
January	1- 4	Quadrantids	A constellation now included in Boötes
April	9-23	Lyrids	Lyra (constellation)
May	1- 6	May Aquarids	Aquarius (constellation)
July	26-31	Aquarids	Aquarius (constellation)
August	10-14	Perseids	Perseus (constellation)
October	9-10	Giacobinids	Comet Giacobini-Zinner
October	18-23	Orionids	Orion (constellation)
November	14-18	Leonids	Leo (constellation)
December	10-13	Geminids	Gemini (constellation)

MEASURING HEIGHT AND VELOCITY

To determine the height and velocity of meteors, astronomers have followed procedures like this. Two astronomers who are 50 miles apart observe the same meteor. Suppose one is at A and the other observer is at C, which is 50 miles away. Both of them see the meteor at B. One observer measures the angle at A and the other observer measures the angle at C. Now two angles of the triangle are known, and the base line is 50 miles. Since three parts of the triangle are known, we can solve for BD, which would be the height of the meteor above the earth.

If the duration of the meteor is timed, and the position where it disappears is noted, its velocity can be computed. The length of the

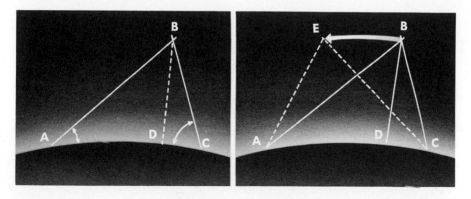

line *BE* can be determined. Suppose it was found to be 20 miles, and suppose the duration of the light streak was 2 seconds, the velocity of the meteor would be 10 mps.

When a meteoroid penetrates earth's atmosphere and falls to earth, it is called a meteorite. Meteorites are relatively rare, although a hundred or so fall to earth for every one that is positively identified. Meteorites interest scientists a great deal, for they are the only tangible material that they have from outer space. Astronomers obtain information by studying light, radio waves, infrared waves, ultraviolet waves, and other forms of energy received on earth. But energy cannot be touched or studied chemically and microscopically the way that meteorites can.

Meteorites vary a great deal in size, shape, and composition. However, they are classified into three large groups according to the most prominent substance they contain. Iron meteorites are called siderites, stony meteorites are aerolites, and those that are made of both stone and iron are called siderolites.

Forty different chemical elements have been found in meteorites. The most abundant of these are: iron, oxygen, silicon, magnesium, nickel, sulfur, calcium, and aluminum.

If you should find an isolated piece of iron, chances are that you have a meteorite. It probably is not a meteorite if you find it near a known iron deposit. Test it with a magnet to see if it is iron, and compare its weight with a piece of stone of the same size. Iron should weigh considerably more. A positive identification to determine whether your piece of iron is an iron meteorite is the presence of lines called Widmanstaetten lines. Polish the iron and then etch the polished surface with dilute hydrochloric acid. (CAUTION: Wash immediately if the acid gets on your fingers.) Polish the iron again. If streaks appear (Widmanstaetten lines) you have a meteorite, and there is no question about it.

It is difficult to go further in identification of meteorites unless you have technical equipment. Therefore, we suggest that, if you suspect that you have found a meteorite, you send it to the geology department of your local college or museum. They will subject it to tests and give you an answer you may rely upon. Incidentally, although thousands of specimens have been sent to the American Museum, not one has been identified as a meteorite.

While you are sky watching, it may occur to you that meteor watching could be a rather dangerous occupation. One of the meteoroids might fall to earth, and it would be tragic if you happened to be in the path of it. Let us assure you that there is little cause for worry. Actually, there is only one proved case of a person being struck by a meteorite. In 1954 a woman in Sylacauga, Alabama, was struck in the thigh by a meteorite. She was not injured seriously because the meteorite passed through the roof and a ceiling before it struck her. There have been other reports of people being struck by meteorites, but they are unconfirmed.

There have been a few close calls with meteorites. In 1847 a forty-pound meteorite crashed into a house in Bohemia. Fortunately, it missed three children in the house at the time. A few years ago a meteorite fell into a garden patch near Auckland, New Zealand, barely missing a woman who was working there.

There have been several spectacular collisions of meteorites with the earth. In 1908 a number of meteorites fell in Siberia. Fifteen hundred reindeer were killed by them, and trees covering an area of one hundred square miles were felled. People four hundred miles away reported hearing the noise of impact.

In prehistory a meteorite fell in Arizona. It must have been of great size, for it made a crater some 4,200 feet across, and almost 600 feet deep. The Chubb Crater in Quebec is about two and one half times larger than the Arizona Crater. We know little about this formation, although scientists are learning more from studies now in process. Also, observations now being made from airplanes reveal that there are numerous ancient craters throughout the world, perhaps produced by meteorites that crashed into the planet millenniums ago.

We do not know the origin of meteorites, but many astronomers believe that they originate in the asteroid belt. There is a great gap between the orbits of Mars and Jupiter. Perhaps a planet existed in that region long ago, and perhaps some great explosion occurred which caused the planet to disintegrate. The remains of the planet are the asteroids.

Occasionally the orbit of a stray asteroid cuts across earth's orbit, and we collide with the object. Since the asteroids are large, they do not burn up as they pass through our atmosphere and so they reach earth's surface; they become meteorites.

There are probably thousands of asteroids. Several hundred of them have been observed and studied. Some of those which have come closest to the earth are tabulated here, together with interesting information about them.

Asteroid	Discovered (year)	Least Distance from Earth	Revolution in Years	Estimated Diameter (miles)
433 Eros	1898	13,900,000	1.76	20 (longest dimension)
1221 Amor	1932	10,400,000	2.67	1.5
Apollo	1932	2,500,000	1.81	1.0
Adonis	1936	1,200,000	2.76	1.0
Hermes	1937	475,000	2.00	.75

In many cases when objects are listed in order of their distance from earth, the moon is given as the nearest neighbor, then Venus, and so on. To be correct, the asteroids should be mentioned also. All of the above have come much closer to us than Venus, which is 26 million miles away at its closest.

MAN-MADE SATELLITES

9

In 1957 sky watchers were able to observe new and exciting objects, for on October 4 of that year the first artificial satellite was placed in orbit. Since that time, there has always been at least one of these objects revolving about the earth. Some of them are much more visible than others; but all of them challenge the skill and patience of the observer.

Artificial satellites can be seen only at twilight. Twilight is the period before sunrise, and also the period that follows sunset. Morning and evening twilight both last about one and one-half hours. At these times the satellites reflect sunlight to our eyes, but the sky itself is dark. We see a bright object against a dark background.

Satellites carry no lights of their own. Some people have suggested that they should, but the idea is not a good one because a bright light would use a large amount of electricity. The weight of the batteries required to produce the electricity would be prohibitive. Therefore, satellites receive illumination from the sun alone. During the daytime the satellites are lighted, but we cannot see them because the sky is brightly lighted also. We see objects only by contrast. For example, we can see a dark object against a light background easily, but it is hard to see a dark object against a dark background. There is no contrast between a satellite and the daytime sky, both are bright; therefore, we see nothing.

When it is on the night side of the earth, a satellite is not lighted by the sun. Since there is no light to be reflected to earth, satellites are invisible at nighttime. Only at dusk and dawn are conditions just right for observing satellites. But even then we may not be able to see them.

The sky may be overcast; this would make observation impossible. The observer might not know where to look, and so the satellite may come and go unnoticed. Also, the satellite may be very low in the sky. Generally speaking, objects lower than about 12° above the horizon are not observable.

There are two reasons why the satellite may be low in the sky. First, the satellite may be passing considerably east or west of your location. At 40° north or south of the equator, 1° of longitude equals about 60 miles. Suppose your longitude is 90°, and suppose the twilight pass of the satellite is going to be at 83° or 97° longitude, then it would be about 420 miles east or west of you. You could see the satellite if conditions for seeing were good, but it would appear low in the sky.

Second, the inclination — the angle that the orbit makes with the equator — may be so low that the satellite would never be visible from your latitude. For example, some satellites were revolving at 65° angles to the equator; they reached 65° north and south of the equator. Therefore, it was possible for them to be seen by all the people who lived between these two extremes. Other

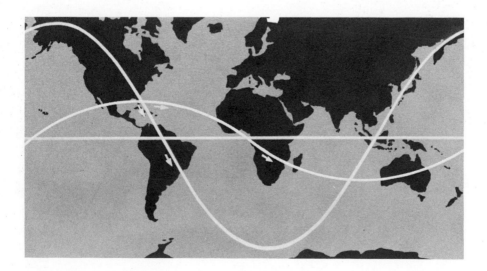

satellites were revolving at angles of 35° to the equator. The highest latitude they reached was 35° N. and 35° S. Only those people who lived within these extremes could see them. People a bit north or south of the extremes might see the satellites also, but they would always be low in the southern or northern skies.

Large satellites and sometimes the last-stage rocket section of the nose cones can be seen quite easily with the naked eye. They reflect so much sunlight that they appear very bright, sometimes as bright as the brightest stars.

Smaller satellites reflect very little light, and so they are too dim to be seen without the aid of binoculars or a telescope. Satellites move very rapidly across the sky (they make a pass across the entire sky in 4 or 5 minutes) and so a wide-field viewer is needed. This means something that can see a rather broad part of the sky at once. A 7×50 monocular has been found effective. This device has moderate ability to concentrate light. It can "see" a considerable amount of the sky, so the used can "find" a moving satellite with it and he can keep the satellite in view. Special monoculars like this are not essential for viewing; ordinary wide-field binoculars work very well.

Sighting a satellite is exciting, for you are observing an object moving 18,000 miles an hour, and one which, an hour later, will be on the other side of the earth, perhaps observed by people in India, China, or Australia.

If you are interested in observing satellites systematically and recording your observations and the positions of your sightings, get in touch with your local newspaper or high school. There may be a Moonwatch team that is still active. Moonwatch teams are groups of observers who were organized during the International Geophysical Year to sight satellites. Many of the teams continue to operate, even though the IGY is over officially.

We are not at all sure about what happens to man-made satellites during the final stages of their life. We know that they accelerate, that the period required to make a revolution decreases as they spiral toward the center of gravity. Also, they must become white hot due to friction with the increasingly denser atmosphere as they approach the surface of the earth. Radar contacts indicate that large satellites break into smaller pieces, probably because of structural weakening as the metals increase in temperature.

If you are lucky, you may be able to see the bright streak of light across the sky which will be the disintegration of an artificial satellite. And, if you are extremely fortunate, you may be able to photograph the event and so provide more evidence to prove that satellites really do end their existence in these meteorlike streaks of light.

Sky watching is exciting, for it is always interesting to see and understand events that are occurring all around us. Casual observations of the sky give some satisfaction, but the real pleasure comes from keeping records of observations, from improving the precision of sightings. Be your own critic, make demands upon yourself, keep accurate records, do not be content with slipshod results; and sky watching will become a lasting interest, one that will be with you all your life and wherever you go.

FOR FURTHER READING

BOOKS

Adler, Irving. *The Stars: Stepping Stones into Space*, The John Day Company, New York, 1956.

Branley, Franklyn M. *Mars*, Thomas Y. Crowell Company, New York, 1955.

Branley, Franklyn M. *The Nine Planets*, Thomas Y. Crowell Company, New York, 1958.

Branley, Franklyn M. *Solar Energy*, Thomas Y. Crowell Company, New York, 1957.

Chamberlain, Joseph M., and Nicholson, Thomas D. *Planets, Stars and Space*, Creative Education Society, 1957.

Freeman, Ira and Mae. *Fun with Astronomy*, Random House, Inc., New York, 1953.

Hood, Peter. *How Time Is Measured*, Oxford University Press, New York, 1955.

Howard, N. E. *Handbook for Observing the Satellites*, Thomas Y. Crowell Company, New York, 1958.

Neely, Henry M. *The Stars by Clock and Fist*, Viking Press, New York, 1956.

Newton, R., and Mayall, Margaret. *Sundials: How to Know, Use and Make Them*, Charles T. Branford Company, Newton Centre, Mass.

Nicholson, Thomas D. *The Adventure Book of Stars*, Capitol Publishing Company, New York.

Olcott, William, and Mayall, R. Newton and Margaret. *Field Book of the Skies*, G. P. Putnam's & Sons, New York, 1954.

Pickering, James S. *The Stars Are Yours*, The Macmillan Company, New York, 1953.

The Editors of *Popular Science*. *Everybody's Guide to Astronomy*, Grosset and Dunlap, New York, 1949.

Zarchy, Harry. *Wheel of Time*, Thomas Y. Crowell Company, New York, 1957.

Zim, Herbert S. *Shooting Stars*, William Morrow and Company, New York, 1958.

MAGAZINES

Natural History Magazine. American Museum of Natural History, 79th Street and Central Park West, New York 24, New York.

Sky and Telescope. Sky Publishing Company, 60 Garden Street, Cambridge, Massachusetts.

INDEX

Acamar, 73, 74
Achernar, 73, 74
Adonis, 100
aerolites, 97
Albireo, 71, 72
Aldebaran, 75, 76
Algenib, 73, 74
Alioth, 69, 70
Alkaid, 69, 70
Almach, 73, 74
Alnilam, 75, 76
Alphard, 69, 70, 75, 76
Alphecca, 69, 70, 71, 72
Alpheratz, 72, 73, 74
Al Suhail, 75, 76
Altair, 68, 70, 71, 72
altitude, determining of, 4-6, 10-12, 96
American Meteor Society, 95
Amor, 100
analemma, 21-23
Andromeda, 73, 74
Andromedes, the, 95
Antares, 68, 71, 72
Apollo, 100
apparent motion, 54-56, 80
Aquarids, the, 96
Aquarius, 96
Arcturus, 68, 69, 70
Arend-Roland comet, 86
Aries, 73, 74
Arizona Crater, 99
asteroids, 100
astrolabe, 5-7, 11
atmosphere:
  and artificial satellites, 105
  and auroras, 61-62
  light refraction by, 16-17, 32, 34-35

meteoroids in, 92-94, 97
  of the planets, 57
Auriga, 75, 76
aurora australis, 59
aurora borealis, 58-59
Auroral Data Center, 65
auroras, 13, 58-65
autumn, see fall
azimuth, 4-7

Baily, Francis, 14
Baily's Beads, 14
Bellatrix, 68
Betelgeuse, 68, 74, 75
Big Dipper, 3, 69, 70, 74, 76, 77, 78, 81-82
Birkeland, Olaf Kristian, 62
bolide, 93
Boötes, 96
Brahe, Tycho, 1

camera, see photographs
Canis Major, 74, 75
Canopus, 75, 76
Capella, 73, 74, 75, 76
Caph, 73, 74, 76, 77
Cassiopeia, 73, 74, 76, 77, 78
Castor, 75, 76
celestial equator, 38-41
Chicago, Ill.:
  latitude of, 18
  true north for, 19
Chubb Crater, 99
Comet Giacobini-Zinner, 96
Comet Mrkos, 86
comets, 84-91
compass, magnetic, 19
constellations (see also stars), 68-78, 95-96

About the Author

FRANKLYN M. BRANLEY is Associate Astronomer at the American Museum-Hayden Planetarium. There he directs the educational program which includes courses in astronomy, navigation, and meteorology. He holds degrees from New Paltz State Teachers College, New York University, and Columbia University. His home is in New Jersey.

Dr. Branley is the author of *The Nine Planets; Exploring by Satellite: The Story of Project Vanguard; Mars; Experiments in the Principles of Space Travel;* and *Solar Energy,* and he is coauthor, with Dr. Nelson F. Beeler, of many excellent science experiment books for young people.

About the Artist

HELMUT K. WIMMER was born in Munich, Germany, and came to the United States in 1954. He joined the Hayden Planetarium immediately as staff artist.

Mr. Wimmer is also a sculptor and makes architectural models in his free time.

With his wife and daughter, Mr. Wimmer enjoys mountain climbing, skating, skiing, and swimming.

The Wimmers, too, live in New Jersey.